ADVANCED TOPICS IN MECHANICS

Minds·On PHYSICS

Activities & Reader

ADVANCED TOPICS IN MECHANICS

Minds·On PHYSICS

Activities & Reader

William J. Leonard
Robert J. Dufresne
William J. Gerace
Jose P. Mestre

The University of Massachusetts
Physics Education Research Group

KENDALL/HUNT PUBLISHING COMPANY
4050 Westmark Drive   Dubuque, Iowa 52002

Also available in the Minds•On Physics Series

Minds•On Physics: Motion / Activities & Reader

Teacher's Guide to accompany Minds•On Physics: Motion

Minds•On Physics: Interactions / Activities & Reader

Teacher's Guide to accompany Minds•On Physics: Interactions

Minds•On Physics: Conservation Laws & Concept-Based Problem Solving / Activities & Reader

Teacher's Guide to accompany Minds•On Physics: Conservation Laws & Concept-Based Problem Solving

Minds•On Physics: Fundamental Forces & Fields / Activities & Reader

Teacher's Guide to accompany Minds•On Physics: Fundamental Forces & Fields

Minds•On Physics: Complex Systems / Activities & Reader

Teacher's Guide to accompany Minds•On Physics: Complex Systems

Teacher's Guide to accompany Minds•On Physics: Advanced Topics in Mechanics

Author Address for Correspondence

William J. Leonard
Department of Physics & Astronomy
Box 34525
University of Massachusetts
Amherst, MA 01003–4525 USA

e-mail: WJLEONARD@phast.umass.edu

Cover Photos: Image of roller coaster "The Dragon" courtesy of Adventureland Park, Des Moines, Iowa. Tennis player image © 1997 PhotoDisc. All other images courtesy of Corel.

ISBN 0-7872-5411-8

This book was prepared with the support of NSF Grant: ESI 9255713. However, any opinions, findings, conclusions and or recommendations herein are those of the authors and do not necessarily reflect the views of NSF.

Printed in the United States of America
10 9 8 7 6 5 4 3 2 1

Contents

Reader
ADVANCED TOPICS IN MECHANICS

CHAPTER 1. Circular, Projectile & Relative Motion

Reader (continued)

continued

Reader (continued)

Reader (continued)

continued

Reader (continued)

1.3 RELATIVE MOTION (continued)

Reader (continued)

CHAPTER 2. Rotational Motion

continued

Reader (continued)

Reader (continued)

How to Use this Book

The activities in this book are designed to get you *thinking about* and *doing* physics — in a way that is a lot closer to the way professional scientists think about and do science. You will learn by communicating your ideas with your teacher and with other students, and by trying to make sense of the ideas presented in the book.

While you are studying this material, you might be required to memorize some definitions, some vocabulary, and some other basic information, but you should <u>not</u> try to memorize the answers to specific questions and problems. Answer should *make sense to you*. If they do not make sense to you, then you probably should go back and change how you think about the problem or situation. Even if everyone else seems to understand something, please do not give up! Keep trying until it makes sense to you.

We want *everyone* in the class to understand physics, and we sincerely believe that everyone *can* learn to understand physics, because the activities are intended to help everyone develop the skills needed to learn and to do physics. When necessary, your teacher and your classmates should be able to help you. Find out how they think about a problem or situation, and adapt their ideas to your own way of thinking. And if you are helping someone else, remember that everyone learns at a different rate, so please be patient.

This style of learning requires a lot of dedication and work, especially if you are not familiar with the style. In the short run, this style might seem impossible and not worth the extra effort. But in the long run, it is definitely worth it. We really, really want you to memorize *as little as possible*. Focus on the ideas that are most widely useful, and learn how to use these to derive the relationships you might need to answer a question or solve a problem. You will be able to solve lots of problems using this approach, and you will develop skills that will be useful in any field you might choose to enter. Remember that physics is one way — among many — of looking at the natural world. It's a way of analyzing, evaluating, describing, explaining, and predicting the behavior of objects and collections of objects.

Acknowledgments

The *concept-based problem-solving* approach to learning is the way Bill Gerace has taught hundreds of graduate and undergraduate students at the University of Massachusetts. It is his approach that has been refined, modified, and adapted to create the activities in this book.

We are deeply grateful to the National Science Foundation for funding the pilot project, *Materials for Developing Concept-Based Problem-Solving Skills in Physics*, under grant MDR–9050213. Although we had no prior experience writing materials for high-school physics, the Foundation reasoned that as experts in both physics and cognitive research, we were uniquely qualified to bring a fresh outlook to the task. We thank NSF also for funding the renewal, *Minds-On Physics: An Integrated Curriculum for Developing Concept-Based Problem Solving in Physics*, under grant ESI–9255713. The materials in this book are a direct result of this funding and are also evidence of how federal support can impact education and stimulate reform. We thank Gerhard Salinger, our project director at NSF, for his unwavering support of our approach and his many suggestions.

We are very fortunate to have found four wonderful teachers who were willing to try a different approach to teaching physics by field-testing those first 24 "modules" of the pilot project: Charlie Camp (Amherst Regional HS, Amherst, MA), Mike Cunha (Weaver HS, Hartford, CT), Steve Degon (Central HS, Springfield, MA) and Hughes Pack (Northfield–Mount Hermon School, Northfield, MA). They let us into their classrooms and let us see first-hand how their students dealt with the approach. Their numerous suggestions have improved the materials and the approach greatly.

We also thank all the teachers who have field-tested Minds•On Physics activities: Jane Barrett (Howard School of Academics & Technology, Chattanooga, TN), Larry Blanchard (Warren Easton HS, New Orleans, LA), Roger Blough (Tyner HS, Chattanooga, TN), Gaby Blum (Monument Mountain Regional HS, Great Barrington, MA), Charlie Camp (ARHS), Jim Carter (Saugus HS, Saugus, MA), Jack Czajkowski (Great Falls Middle School, Montague, MA), John Dark (Brainerd HS, Chattanooga, TN), Steve Degon (Central HS), Ed Eckel (Georgetown Day School, Washington, DC), Jen DuBois (NMH), Jake Foster (Hixson HS, Hixson, TN), Bill Fraser (Chattanooga Phoenix School 3, Chattanooga, TN), Ken Gano (Hixson HS), Dennis Gilbert (Taconic HS, Pittsfield, MA), Craig Hefner (NMH), Ray Janke (Chicopee HS, Chicopee, MA), Aaron Kropf (Springfield HS of Science & Technology, Springfield, MA), Bernie Lally

(Chicopee HS), Michael Oliphant (Millis HS, Millis, MA), Hughes Pack (NMH), Jerry Pate (Chattanooga School for Arts and Sciences, Chattanooga, TN), Kirk Rau (Tyner HS), Jessie Royal (Dade County HS, Trenton, GA), Cheryl Ryan (Hoosac Valley Regional HS, Adams, MA), John Safko (The University of South Carolina, Columbia, SC), Glenda Schmidt (Slidell HS, Slidell, LA), Lisa Schmitt (NMH), Steve Schultheis (Saugus HS), Lance Simpson (NMH), Mark Walcroft (Taconic HS), Mark Wenig (CSAS), Maxine Willis (Gettysburg HS, Gettysburg, PA), Melany O'Connor (NMH), and Tom Winn (McMain HS, New Orleans, LA). They often had little warning about what and when materials would arrive, and usually had just a few days to prepare themselves to do the activities in class. We appreciate their patience and understanding. We also thank them for recommending that we create extensive teacher support materials. Although this addition has nearly doubled the scope of the project, it is a welcome change, and every teacher who uses the Minds•On Physics materials is indebted to them.

We thank Kris Chapman and Maggie Coffin for many of the drawings used in the activities. They brought a style and grace to the figures that none of us could ever match. We thank Ian Beatty for creating the Town of King's Court. We also thank Gary Bradway (Berkshire Community College, Pittsfield, MA), for his frequent help with conceptualizing and revising the early activities; Jerry Touger (Curry College, Milton, MA), for his help writing the Reader; and George Collison (The Concord Consortium, Concord, MA), for showing us how hands-on activities may be combined with minds-on activities.

Many thanks to Allan Feldman (University of Massachusetts, Amherst, MA) and the rest of his evaluation team (Karla, Jim, Ed, Sonal, and Aaron) for evaluating the materials and its implementation.

We are thankful to Kendall/Hunt for publishing these materials. We are particularly thankful to the people at K/H for their many ideas and suggestions, especially regarding the format and style of these materials.

Special thanks also to all our friends and relatives.

Bill Leonard
Bob Dufresne
Bill Gerace
Jose Mestre

The UMass Physics Education Research Group
Department of Physics & Astronomy
Box 34525
University of Massachusetts
Amherst, MA 01003-4525 USA

Visit us on the Web at http://www-perg.phast.umass.edu/

Activities

AT·1–23:
ADVANCED TOPICS IN MECHANICS

Exploring Ideas About Circular Motion

Purpose and Expected Outcome

In this activity, you will begin studying circular motion more formally than you have until now. You already know all the concepts about the motion of objects and their interactions with the world. You need to review what you have learned so far, and learn how to apply concepts to more complicated situations.

Prior Experience / Knowledge Needed

You need to know basic motion concepts, such as *velocity* and *acceleration*, as well as ideas related to interactions, such as *free-body diagrams*, *force*, and *net force*.

Explanation of Activity

There are two parts in this activity. In the first part, you will draw free-body diagrams for objects moving along circular arcs. In the second part, you will analyze the acceleration of objects moving along circular arcs.

PART A: Drawing Valid Free-Body Diagrams

For each of the following situations, draw a free-body diagram showing all the forces exerted on the object going in a circle. Be prepared to explain your drawings to your classmates.

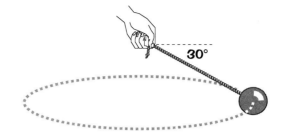

A1. A ball is swung in a horizontal circle as shown. Draw the free-body diagram for the ball when it is at its rightmost point in the circle.

A2. A car is traveling at constant speed around a curve in the road.

A3. A race car is traveling at constant speed around a banked curve. The angle of the banked curve is about 15°.

A4. The Earth is traveling around the Sun.

A5. You are at rest on a spinning Earth. In addition to drawing a free-body diagram for yourself, draw the Earth and indicate the North and South Poles as well as your location on the Earth.

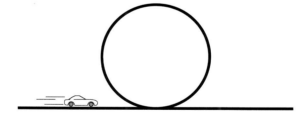

A6. A toy race car travels in a vertical circle around a curved length of track as shown. Draw the free-body diagram for the car when it is at its highest point.

A7. A pendulum is held horizontally as shown and released from rest. Draw a free-body diagram for the ball at each of the five locations indicated.

(a) Just after being released.
(b) At 45° below the horizontal.
(c) When the string is vertical.
(d) Again, at 45° below the horizontal.
(e) When the ball is at its highest point on the right-hand side.

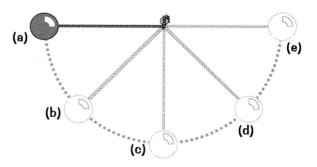

PART B: Analyzing the Acceleration

For each of the following situations, (a) indicate the direction of the acceleration, and (b) answer a question about the forces exerted in the situation. Be prepared to discuss your answers with your classmates.

B1. A ball is swung in a horizontal circle as shown.
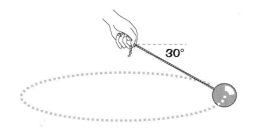

    (a) At the instant shown, what is the direction of the acceleration of the ball?

    (b) Which force is most responsible for keeping the ball traveling in a circle?

B2. A car is traveling at constant speed around a curve in the road.

    (a) What is the direction of the car's acceleration?

    (b) What force(s) must be present to allow the car to go around the curve without going off the road?

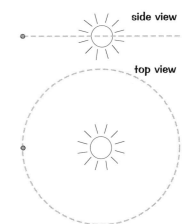

B3. A race car is traveling at constant speed around a banked curve. The angle of the banked curve is about 15°.

    (a) What is the direction of the car's acceleration?

    (b) Which forces on the car <u>must</u> be present?

B4. The Earth is traveling around the Sun as shown in the side and top views to the right.

    (a) What is the direction of the Earth's acceleration?

    (b) How many forces are exerted on the Earth?

B5. You have a friend in South Africa located at the **x** in the drawing below. When your friend is at rest on a spinning Earth,

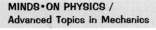

    (a) what is the direction of his acceleration?

    (b) what force(s) must be present in order to cause the observed acceleration?

Reflection

R1. (a) Make a list of all the forces in your free-body diagrams in part A.

(b) Compare your list to the forces described in Table of Common Forces at the end of **Book 2: Interactions**. What forces in your list are <u>not</u> found in the table? Why are these forces missing from the table?

R2. In situation B1, the acceleration of the ball is horizontal, yet neither of the two forces on the ball (ignoring air resistance) is horizontal. This means that none of the forces on the ball is parallel to the acceleration. In part B, there are two more situations for which there is no force parallel to the acceleration.

(a) Identify these two other situations.

(b) How is it possible for the acceleration to have a direction different than every force exerted on the object?

(c) Describe two examples of straight-line motion in which there is no force parallel to the acceleration.

R3. Reconsider situation B5, in which a person at rest in South Africa is traveling in a circle. Now imagine another person at the equator, also at rest.

(a) Which person is traveling in the larger circle? Explain.

(b) Which person has the larger speed? Explain.

(c) Which person has the larger acceleration? Explain.

R4. Reconsider situation A7, in which a ball is attached to a string and is released from rest.

(a) What is the direction of the net force on the ball just after the ball is released?

(b) What must be the direction of the acceleration just after the ball is released?

(c) How is this possible? What are some of the features of this situation that are different from all the other situations?

Finding Acceleration for Circular Motion

Purpose and Expected Outcome

In this activity you will use the definition of acceleration to determine its magnitude and direction for an object traveling in a circle at constant speed. You will understand better what is meant by taking smaller and smaller time intervals to show how the average acceleration eventually reaches the instantaneous acceleration.

Prior Experience / Knowledge Needed

You need to know the definition of acceleration as the change in velocity per unit time. You also need to know how to find the difference between two vector quantities. You should be familiar with other motion quantities, such as position and speed, for objects moving along circular arcs.

Explanation of Activity

There are two parts in this activity. In the first part, you will review how to compute and estimate motion quantities for an object traveling in a circle. In the second part, you will compute the average acceleration for increasingly smaller time intervals.

PART A: Getting Started

A ball is attached to a metal rod, which rotates at a constant speed using a motor attached to the pivot. The radius of the circular path traced by the ball is R = 8cm, and the ball completes one full revolution every 12 seconds. The arrangement is shown at time t = 0s.

Answer the questions below about this situation.

A1. (a) Through how many degrees of angle does the rod sweep each second?

(b) How much distance does the ball cover every second? Explain.

(c) What is the relationship between the distance traveled by the ball and the change in angle of the rod?

A2. (a) Compute the speed of the ball. Explain how you did it.

(b) Is the speed of the ball constant or changing? Explain.

(c) Compute the velocity of the ball at the instant shown. Explain.

(d) Is the velocity of the ball constant or changing? Explain.

(e) Is the ball accelerating? Explain.

A3. On a separate sheet of paper, make a strobe diagram of this situation showing the locations and velocities of the ball from t = 0s to t = 6s.

A4. (a) Estimate the ball's <u>change</u> in velocity between $t = 2^{1}/_{2}$s and $t = 3^{1}/_{2}$s. Explain.

(b) Where is the ball located at t = 3s?

(c) Estimate the ball's average acceleration between $t = 2^{1}/_{2}$s and $t = 3^{1}/_{2}$s. Explain.

*** *This is an estimate of the instantaneous acceleration of the ball at t = 3s.* ***

A5. (a) Where is the ball located at t = 6s?

(b) Estimate the instantaneous acceleration of the ball at t = 6s.

A6. For each of the quantities listed below, determine which would change when (a) <u>only</u> the time for one revolution is changed to 4 seconds, and (b) <u>only</u> the radius of the circle is changed to 24cm. Would the quantities become larger or smaller? By what factor?

❏ speed of the ball

❏ velocity of the ball

❏ average acceleration

❏ instantaneous acceleration

❏ degrees of angle swept by rod every second

❏ distance covered by the ball every second

❏ change in velocity between $t = 2^{1}/_{2}$s and $t = 3^{1}/_{2}$s

❏ location of the ball at t = 3s

PART B: Finding the Magnitude and Direction of Acceleration

A ball is attached to a metal rod, which rotates at a constant speed using a motor attached to the pivot. (See the diagram below.) The radius of the circular path traced by the ball is $R = 100$cm, and the ball is traveling at a constant speed of $v = 50$cm/s. You will use this situation throughout this part, although the values of R and v will be changed near the end.

The goal is to determine the instantaneous acceleration of the ball when it is located on the positive x-axis. To do this you will consider a time interval that starts just before the ball reaches the x-axis and ends just afterwards. By filling in the table below, you will compute the average acceleration of the ball for increasingly smaller time intervals. You will then be able to infer what the instantaneous acceleration must be.

B1. For each quantity listed below, draw a picture to represent the quantity, and indicate the relationship you will use to compute it.

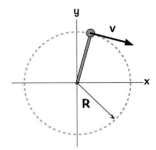

(a) Δs, the distance traveled by the ball during Δt

(b) $\Delta \theta$, the change in angle of the rod during Δt

(c) $\Delta \mathbf{v}$, the change in velocity of the ball during Δt

(d) $\mathbf{a}_{ave}$, the average acceleration of the ball during Δt

Fill in a copy of the table below, using the relationships indicated in B1. Note that R is different for B9 and v is different for B10. Also, the time interval Δt starts just before the ball reaches the x-axis and ends just after the ball reaches the x-axis. Some examples have been filled in. (For vector quantities, the direction is indicated using an arrow.)

	R [cm]	v [cm/s]	Δt [s]	(a) Δs [cm]	(b) $\Delta \theta$ [degrees]	(c) $\Delta \mathbf{v}$ [cm/s]	(d) $\mathbf{a}_{ave}$ [cm/s^2]
B2.	100	50	2.0	100			
B3.	100	50	0.8		22.92		
B4.	100	50	0.4			9.98 ←	
B5.	100	50	0.2				24.99 ←
B6.	100	50	0.04			1.00 ←	
B7.	100	50	0.02		0.573		
B8.	100	50	0.002	0.1			
B9.	300	50	0.2		1.91		
B10.	100	150	0.2			44.83 ←	

Reflection

R1. (a) Based on the table in part B, what do think the instantaneous acceleration of the ball is for $R = 100$cm and $v = 50$cm/s? Explain.

(b) When the radius of the circle is tripled (in B9), does the average acceleration of the ball increase or decrease? By what factor?

(c) When the speed of the ball is tripled (in B10), does the average acceleration of the ball increase or decrease? By what factor?

R2. (a) Use your answers to R1 above to write down an expression for the <u>magnitude</u> of the acceleration for an object moving at constant speed v around a circle of radius R.

(b) What is the <u>direction</u> of the ball's acceleration when it is located on the positive x-axis, as in part B?

(c) How can you find the direction of the ball's acceleration at another location? For example, what is the direction of the acceleration when the ball is located on the negative y-axis? Explain.

R3. Does this result (above in R2) surprise you? What about it surprises you? Explain.

R4. Explain why we asked you to focus on the ball when it was on the positive x-axis, rather than when it was at a random or arbitrary point. Did the choice make the calculations easier or more convenient in any way? Explain. What other points (on the circle) would have been equally convenient? Explain.

R5. What is the definition of acceleration, and how is it related to the definition of average acceleration? Which questions in part B helped you to find the instantaneous acceleration? What do you suppose was the purpose of all the other questions in part B?

R6. If the arrangement in part B spins counterclockwise (rather than clockwise) how will the acceleration be different when the ball reaches the positive x-axis? Explain.

Minds•On Physics Activity AT·3

Finding Radial Acceleration for Circular Motion

Purpose and Expected Outcome

In this activity you will learn how to compute the acceleration in a variety of situations.

Prior Experience / Knowledge Needed

You should be familiar with the relationship between acceleration, speed, and radius for an object traveling in a circle at constant speed. You should know some basic trigonometry.

RADIAL (OR CENTRIPETAL) ACCELERATION

Radial acceleration is a term used to denote the component of the acceleration perpendicular to the velocity of an object moving along a curved path (see diagram). The radial acceleration points toward the center of the circle that matches the curvature of the path followed by the object.

Using the definition of acceleration ($\mathbf{a} \equiv \Delta\mathbf{v}/\Delta t$; Δt very small), we can rewrite the magnitude of the radial acceleration to be:

$$a_r = \frac{v^2}{R_c}$$

magnitude of radial acceleration

where v is the speed of the object and R_c is the *radius of curvature* of the circle that matches the curvature of the path. This expression is true for all motion, whether the speed is constant or changing, and whether the curvature of the path is constant or changing. Whenever an object's direction of motion is changing, it has a non-zero radial acceleration. (Whenever its <u>speed</u> is changing, it has a non-zero component of acceleration parallel to the direction of motion. This is covered in the next activity.)

The radial acceleration is sometimes called *centripetal* acceleration, which is denoted a_c.

Explanation of Activity

For each situation, determine the magnitude and direction of the radial acceleration.

A1. A ball is attached to a metal rod, which rotates in a circle at constant speed using a motor attached to the pivot. The arrangement completes one revolution every 15 seconds, and the length of the rod is 5cm.

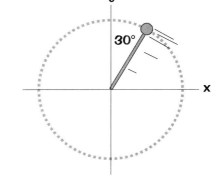

    (a) Find the magnitude of the radial acceleration of the ball at the instant shown.

    (b) Find the *x*-component of the radial acceleration of the ball.

    (c) Find the radial acceleration of the ball when it is on the negative *x*-axis.

A2. Compute the radial acceleration of a block sliding down a frictionless inclined plane as shown. Explain.

A3. A ball is attached to a flexible, 25cm cord and swung in a horizontal circle as shown. The ball travels 5 complete revolutions roughly every 4 seconds.

    (a) Find the radial acceleration of the ball at the instant shown.

    (b) Find the vertical component of the radial acceleration at the instant shown.

    (c) Find the horizontal component of the radial acceleration at the instant shown.

A4. A 200g ball is attached to a 20cm-long cord and released from rest when the cord is horizontal.

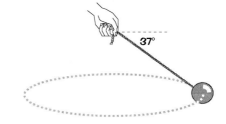

    (a) What is the radial acceleration of the ball when it is at its lowest point?

    (b) How does this value compare to the acceleration of the ball when it drops freely in a gravitational field?

A5. (a) Estimate your acceleration as you are sitting in your seat (on a spinning Earth!). Who in your classroom has the largest acceleration? the smallest? Explain.

    (b) Estimate the acceleration of a person standing near the South Pole.

    (c) Estimate the acceleration of a person standing on the Equator.

Reflection

R1. (a) Of the three people in situation A5, whose motion has the largest radius of curvature as they rotate on a spinning Earth: you, someone at the South Pole, or someone on the Equator? Explain. Whose motion has the smallest radius of curvature? Explain.

   (b) Who has the largest acceleration, or are they all the same? Explain. Who has the smallest acceleration? Explain.

   (c) Did you consider the spinning Earth when you found the accelerations in A1–A4? Why or why not? Should you consider the spinning Earth?

R2. Reconsider situation A1, in which a ball travels in a circle at constant speed.

   (a) If the rate of rotation is doubled, but the length of the rod stays the same, will the radial acceleration change? If so, how? (I.e., will the acceleration get larger, get smaller, or stay the same? By what factor will it change?)

   (b) If the length of the rod is doubled, but the rate of rotation stays the same, will the radial acceleration change? If so, how?

   (c) If the direction of rotation is reversed (that is, the ball moves at the same speed, but clockwise rather than counterclockwise) will the radial acceleration change? If so, how?

R3. For two of the situations in this activity, the radial acceleration is zero. Which two? What other quantity is also zero for both of these situations?

R4. For two of the situations in this activity, there is no force that has the same direction as the acceleration. Which two? How is it possible for there to be an acceleration without a force in the same direction? Explain.

R5. Using a ball and a piece of string, create a situation in which the acceleration of the ball is larger than $9.8 m/s^2$ at all times. Describe how you did it. Estimate the acceleration of the ball.

R6. Reconsider situation A4, in which a ball is attached to a string and released from rest when the string is horizontal.

   (a) If the mass of the ball is quadrupled to 800g, will the radial acceleration of the ball be the same or different when it reaches its lowest point? If different, how will it change? Explain. If the same, explain why the acceleration is the same.

   (b) If the string is replaced with a very light metal rod (such as a spoke from a bicycle wheel), will the radial acceleration of the ball be the same or different when it reaches its lowest point? Explain.

Finding Tangential Acceleration for Circular Motion

Purpose and Expected Outcome

You will learn how to determine the tangential acceleration in a variety of situations.

Prior Experience / Knowledge Needed

You should know Newton's laws and be able to apply them to different situations. You should know some basic trigonometry.

TANGENTIAL ACCELERATION

The component of the acceleration <u>parallel</u> to the velocity is called the *tangential acceleration*. It is non-zero whenever the <u>speed</u> of an object is changing.

Using the definition of acceleration ($\mathbf{a} \equiv \Delta\mathbf{v}/\Delta t$; Δt very small), we can rewrite the magnitude of the tangential acceleration a_t to be:

$$a_t = \frac{\Delta v}{\Delta t} \quad (\Delta t \text{ small})$$
  magnitude of tangential acceleration

where v is the speed of the object.

A positive a_t means that the speed is increasing, and the direction of a_t is the same as the direction of motion. A negative a_t means that the speed is decreasing, and the direction of a_t is opposite the direction of motion.

In most problem situations we do not know exactly how the speed is changing with time, so we cannot use this relationship to determine a_t. However, in many situations, we know the forces parallel to the direction of motion, so we can use Newton's 2nd law to determine a_t. Newton's 2nd law parallel to the direction of motion is written:

$$F_{\text{net},t} = m a_t$$
  Newton's 2nd law parallel to the direction of motion

The direction of $F_{\text{net},t}$ is always the same as the direction of a_t.

Explanation of Activity

For each situation, determine the magnitude and direction of the tangential acceleration.

A1. A ball is attached to a light metal rod, which pivots frictionlessly as shown. The arrangement is released from rest as shown. The arrangement rotates clockwise in a vertical circle. The length of the rod is 5cm.

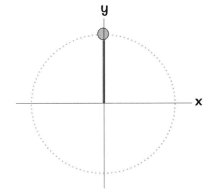

(a) Find the tangential acceleration of the ball as it crosses the positive x-axis.

(b) Find the tangential acceleration of the ball as it crosses the negative y-axis.

(c) Find the tangential acceleration of the ball as it crosses the negative x-axis.

A2. Find the tangential acceleration of a 10kg box being pulled with a force of 30N along a rough surface having a coefficient of kinetic friction of 0.2.

A3. A 200g block slides frictionlessly along a curved surface as shown. Estimate the tangential acceleration of the block at the three instants shown:

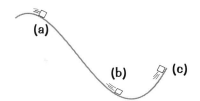

(a) near the top of the hill;

(b) almost to the bottom of the hill; and

(c) after reaching the lowest point possible.

Reflection

R1. Reconsider situation A1, in which a ball travels in a vertical circle. If the arrangement rotated counterclockwise instead of clockwise, would any of your answers change? How?

R2. Reconsider situation A3, in which a block slides frictionlessly along a curved surface. If instead of moving at position (a), the block is released from rest at position (a), would any of your answers change? How?

R3. Does the tangential acceleration depend on the speed of an object? Explain.

Reasoning About
Circular Motion

Purpose and Expected Outcome

In this activity you will reason about the forces exerted on objects undergoing circular motion. You will learn more about how to relate the net force on an object to its acceleration. You will also confront some common points of confusion about circular motion.

Prior Experience / Knowledge Needed

You should be familiar with the relationship between speed, radius of curvature and radial acceleration ($a_r = v^2/R_c$, where v is the speed of the object and R_c is the radius of curvature). You should know how to identify common forces (such as the tension force, the normal force, static and kinetic friction forces, and the spring force), and you should be able to draw free-body diagrams. You should know Newton's 2nd law. You should be familiar with tangential acceleration and be able to determine it in simple situations.

Explanation of Activity

Use your knowledge of circular motion and Newton's 2nd law to answer these questions.

A1. A ball is attached to a flexible cord and swung in a horizontal circle as shown. The angle θ between the cord and the horizontal is less than 45°.

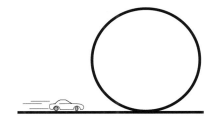

(a) Which is larger, the horizontal or vertical component of the tension force? Explain.

(b) Which is larger, the vertical component of the tension force or the gravitational force? Explain.

(c) Is the acceleration of the ball larger than, smaller than, or the same as the acceleration of a ball falling freely in a gravitational field? Explain.

A2. A toy race car travels around a vertical circle on a curved length of track without ever losing contact.

(a) Where is the car when its radial acceleration is smallest? Explain.

(b) Where is the car when its tangential acceleration is smallest? Explain.

(c) When the car is at the top of the circle, is the acceleration larger than, smaller than, or the same as the acceleration of an object falling freely in a gravitational field? Explain.

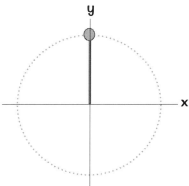

A3. A ball is attached to a light metal rod, which pivots frictionlessly as shown. The arrangement is released from rest at the instant shown.

(a) Where is the ball when its radial acceleration is largest? Explain.

(b) Where is the ball when its tangential acceleration is largest? Explain.

Assume now that the ball is given a strong push at the top (instead of being released from rest).

(c) Would the maximum radial acceleration change? How? Would the maximum tangential acceleration change? How?

continued

A4. A box of mass m is pulled with a force F along a rough surface having a coefficient of friction of μ_k. If the tension in the string is doubled, what will happen to the radial and tangential components of acceleration?

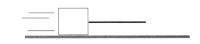

A5. A block is released from rest at the top of a frictionless curved surface and follows the path shown. On a <u>copy</u> of this drawing...

(a) ... indicate the point(s) where the radial acceleration of the block is largest? Explain.

(b) ... indicate the point(s) where the tangential acceleration of the block is largest? Explain.

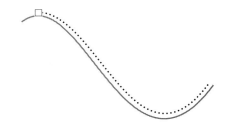

A6. A car is traveling at constant speed around a curve in the road. (The road is not banked.)

(a) Which force on the car is larger, the normal force exerted by the road or the gravitational force? Why?

(b) Which force is larger, the friction force exerted by the road or the gravitational force? Explain.

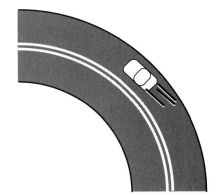

A7. A race car is traveling at a certain speed around a banked curve, whose angle is about 15° above the horizontal. At this particular speed, the friction force between the tires and the road is essentially zero. Which is larger, the force of gravitation or the normal force exerted by the road? Explain.

A8. A car travels along a curved road at roughly constant speed as shown below. On a <u>copy</u> of this diagram...

(a) ... indicate where the acceleration of the car is greatest?

(b) ... indicate where its acceleration is least?

(c) ... indicate where its acceleration is about zero?

(d) ... indicate where the car is most likely to slide.

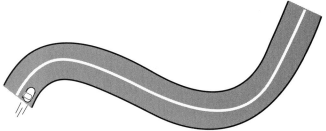

Reflection

R1. (a) For which of the situations did you <u>not</u> draw a free-body diagram? Why not?

    (b) For those situations, draw a free-body diagram, and answer the questions again.

    (c) Do any of your answers change as a result of drawing and using a free-body diagram? Explain.

R2. In <u>three</u> of the situations, the acceleration of the object is vertical (that is, perpendicular to the ground) at least once during its motion.

    (a) Which three situations?

    (b) How do you know the acceleration is vertical?

    (c) Where is the object when its acceleration is vertical?

R3. In <u>at least</u> one situation, the acceleration of the object is horizontal (that is, parallel to the ground) at least once during its motion.

    (a) How many situations? Which one(s)?

    (b) How do you know the acceleration is horizontal?

    (c) Where is the object when its acceleration is horizontal?

R4. (a) Is it possible for the acceleration of an object to have both horizontal and vertical components? Explain. If it is possible, give at least one example.

    (b) Is it possible for the acceleration of an object to have both radial and tangential components? Explain. If it is possible, give at least one example.

    (c) Is it possible for the radial acceleration to have both horizontal and vertical components? Explain. If it is possible, give at least one example.

R5. Reconsider situation A5, in which a block slides frictionlessly along a curved surface.

    (a) Where is the block when its speed is largest?

    (b) Where is the block when its tangential acceleration is largest?

    (c) Are these two locations the same? Why or why not?

    (d) Create a situation in which the tangential acceleration of something is largest at the same time as its speed is smallest.

R6. Reconsider situation A8, in which a car is traveling at roughly constant speed along a curved road. Is your answer to part (d) consistent with your answer to part (a)? Explain.

Solving Problems in Circular Motion

Purpose and Expected Outcome

In this activity you will solve problems involving objects undergoing circular motion. You will learn how to use kinematic information to learn about the forces exerted in a situation and also how to use knowledge of forces to predict the motion of objects traveling in circles.

Prior Experience / Knowledge Needed

You should be familiar with the relationship between speed, radius of curvature and radial acceleration ($a_r = v^2/R_c$, where v is the speed of the object and R_c is the radius of curvature). You should know how to identify common forces (such as the tension force, the normal force, static and kinetic friction forces, and the spring force), and you should be able to draw free-body diagrams. You should know Newton's 2nd law. You should be familiar with tangential acceleration and be able to determine it in simple situations. You should know the definitions associated with work and energy ideas, and you should be able to apply conservation of energy to problem situations.

Explanation of Activity

Use your knowledge of circular motion and Newton's laws to solve these problems.

A1. In science fiction books and movies, space stations are sometimes spinning in order to simulate gravitational conditions on Earth. Imagine a space station that is 600m in diameter.

    (a) Draw a picture showing a cross-section of the space station and show how some people and items might be arranged at different locations in the station. (For instance, show people standing, sleeping, etc. and show tables, chairs, computer monitors, etc.)

    (b) How rapidly must the station rotate to simulate gravitational conditions on Earth?

    (c) What happens to the effect as you consider locations at different distances from the central axis of the station? (That is, where is the simulated gravitation strongest? weakest? non-existent?)

    (d) How would the spinning station affect people of different masses? Would the effect be about the same or noticeably different? Explain.

A2. A 300g ball is attached to a flexible 20cm cord and swung in a horizontal circle as shown. The angle between the cord and the horizontal is about 37°.

    (a) Which force quantities can be determined without knowing the rotation rate of the ball and string? Explain how to find these forces.

    (b) What values do these forces have?

    (c) What motion quantities can be determined from these forces? Explain how to find these motion quantities.

    (d) What values do these motion quantities have?

    (e) What must be the rotation rate for the ball and string?

A3. A 200g ball is attached to a 30cm-long cord and released from rest when the cord is at an angle of 37° as shown.

    (a) What is the tension in the cord immediately after the ball is released?

    (b) What is the tension in the cord when the ball is at its lowest point?

continued

A4. A 240g ball is attached to a light 30cm rod, which pivots frictionlessly as shown. The arrangement is released from rest at the instant shown.

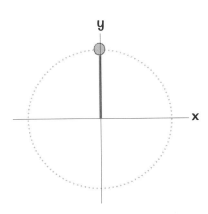

   (a) Determine the force exerted by the rod just after the arrangement is released.

   (b) Determine the force exerted by the rod when the ball is on the *x*-axis.

   (c) Is it possible for the rod to exert no force on the ball? Explain. If it is possible, approximately where does this occur?

A5. A car is traveling at constant speed around an unbanked curve in the road. Tests reveal that a car starts to slide at speeds of about 45mi/h (about 20m/s).

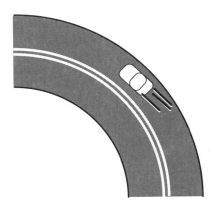

   (a) Estimate the radius of the circle traveled by the car. Explain how you made your estimate. In particular, what quantities did you need to estimate or look up in a reference book?

   (b) What should be the speed limit for this section of road? Explain your reasoning for choosing this speed limit.

A6. If bathroom scales were sensitive enough to measure the effect of the spinning Earth...

   (a) ... does the effect of the spinning Earth increase or decrease your measured weight? Explain.

   (b) ... how large is the maximum possible effect? Explain.

   (c) ... where on the Earth would your measured weight be smallest? largest? Explain.

A7. A popular amusement park ride is a large barrel that spins very rapidly. After everyone is loaded into the barrel, it starts to spin, faster and faster, until it is spinning fast enough for the floor to be removed. The people do not fall even though the floor is gone.

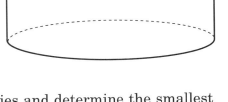

   (a) Explain why the people do not fall.

   (b) For a 68kg person on this ride, determine the values of as many forces as possible.

   (c) What additional information is needed to find the rest of the forces on the person?

   (d) Assume reasonable values for any unknown quantities and determine the smallest rotation rate (in rev/s) that would make the ride work properly.

Reflection

R1. (a) For which of the problems did you <u>not</u> draw a free-body diagram? Why not?

(b) For those problems, draw a free-body diagram, and solve the problem again.

(c) Do any of your answers change as a result of drawing and using a free-body diagram? Explain.

R2. Reconsider situation A2, in which a ball is attached to a cord and swung in a horizontal circle.

(a) Why do you suppose the angle was chosen to be 37°, rather than something else, such as 30°, 45°, or 60°? In other words, what is special about an angle of 37°?

(b) Do you suppose the angle is intended to be "exactly" 37°, or only "approximately" 37°? Explain.

(c) What is the sin(37°)? Is this result exact? What is cos(37°)? Is this result exact? What is tan(37°)? Is this result exact?

(d) What other angle(s) has characteristics similar to 37°? Explain.

R3. (a) For which questions did you use Newton's 2nd law to relate the net force to the acceleration of something?

(b) For which questions did you use a principle other than Newton's 2nd law? Which principles did you use?

R4. Reconsider situation A4, in which a ball is attached to a light rod that rotates frictionlessly around a fixed axle. At least once during the motion of the ball, the force exerted by the rod is zero.

(a) Draw a free-body diagram for the ball at this instant.

(b) Does the ball have a tangential acceleration at this instant? Explain.

(c) Does the ball have a radial acceleration at this instant? Explain.

R5. Reconsider situation A5, in which a car travels around a curve in the road.

(a) What did you ignore in order to make your estimate for the radius of the curve?

(b) Would your answer increase or decrease if you did not ignore these factors? Explain.

Exploring Ideas About Projectile Motion

Purpose and Expected Outcome

In this activity, you will begin studying projectile motion more formally than you have until now. You already know all the concepts about the motion of objects and their interactions with the world. You need to review what you have learned so far, and learn how to apply concepts to more complicated situations.

Prior Experience / Knowledge Needed

You need to know basic motion concepts, such as *velocity* and *acceleration*, as well as ideas related to interactions, such as *free-body diagrams*, *force*, and *net force*. You should have some experience sketching, interpreting, and analyzing graphs of velocity vs. time and position vs. time.

PROJECTILE MOTION

Projectile motion refers to situations in which an object or person travels through the air subject only to the forces of gravitation and air resistance. The *projectile* is the object or person moving through the air. *Simple* projectile motion refers to those situations in which we ignore air resistance.

Explanation of Activity and Example

There are two parts in this activity. In the first part, you will sketch position and velocity graphs for a variety of moving objects and analyze the acceleration of the objects. In the second part, you will explore certain features of trajectories, such as maximum height and the horizontal distance covered.

For each of the following objects, draw sketches of (a) velocity and (b) position vs. time. Then (c), determine the direction of the object's acceleration and state whether your sketches are consistent with this. Be prepared to explain your answers.

E1. A young girl throws a rock from a short cliff as shown.

    (a) Sketch the velocity of the rock as a function of time.

    (b) Sketch the position of the rock as a function of time.

    (c) Is the rock accelerating? If so, what direction is the acceleration? Are your graphs consistent with this?

Answers:

    (a,b) *Graphs of velocity vs. time and position vs. time are shown to the right.*

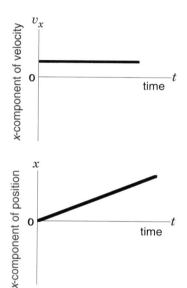

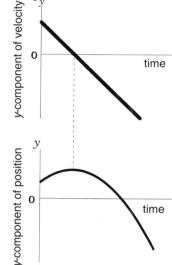

    (c) *Yes, the rock is accelerating in the negative y-direction.*

    Yes, the graphs are consistent with this.

Explanations:

    The velocity has both a horizontal (x-) and a vertical (y-) component, so two graphs are needed to represent velocity vs. time. The x-component of velocity (v_x) is constant, positive, and smaller than the initial value of the y-component of velocity (v_y) because the angle at which the ball is thrown is over 45°. The y-component of velocity starts positive and decreases linearly. Its final value is negative, but larger (in magnitude) than its initial value.

    The position has both an x- and a y-component, so two graphs are needed to represent position vs. time. The x-component of position (x) increases linearly with time. The origin of the coordinate system is chosen to be at the foot of the girl, below the initial position of the rock, so the initial value of x is zero. The y-component of position (y) is positive initially and increasing. At the same instant that v_y is zero, y reaches its maximum value and begins to decrease. The final value of y is negative, and the graph of y vs. t is curved.

continued ⇨

(continued)

We know the rock is accelerating because the only force on the rock is gravitation (ignoring air resistance). This means the acceleration is in the negative y-direction. The graphs are consistent with this because only the y-component of velocity is changing, and the slope is negative throughout the motion of the rock.

A1. A skateboarder flies off a short set of stairs as shown to the right.

(a) Sketch the skateboarder's velocity vs. time.

(b) Sketch the skateboarder's position vs. time.

(c) Is the skateboarder accelerating? If so, what direction is her acceleration? Is this consistent with your sketches in (a) and (b)?

A2. A catapult is used to throw a large rock over the top of a castle wall.

(a) Sketch the rock's velocity vs. time.

(b) Sketch the rock's position vs. time.

(c) Is the rock accelerating? What direction is the rock's acceleration? Is this consistent with your sketches in (a) and (b)?

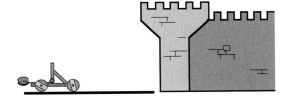

A3. A soccer ball is kicked to the left with an initial speed of 20m/s at an angle of about 37° above the horizontal.

(a) Sketch the velocity vs. time after the ball is kicked.

(b) Sketch the position vs. time after the ball is kicked.

(c) Is the ball accelerating? If so, what direction is the ball's acceleration? Is this consistent with your sketches in (a) and (b)?

A4. The space shuttle is drifting at constant speed far from the Earth as shown. At $t = 0$s, the pilot fires its engines for 12 seconds.

(a) Sketch the velocity vs. time from $t = 0$s to $t = 20$s.

(b) Sketch the position vs. time from $t = 0$s to $t = 20$s.

(c) Is the shuttle accelerating? If so, what direction is the shuttle's acceleration? Is this consistent with your sketches in (a) and (b)?

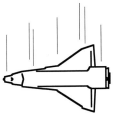

PART B: Comparing Trajectories

For each of the following situations, compare (a) the maximum heights, (b) the times needed to reach the maximum heights, (c) the total horizontal distances traveled, (d) the times needed to land, and (e) the final speeds of the two projectiles. Be prepared to discuss your answers with your classmates. Ignore air resistance throughout.

B1. Two soccer balls are kicked to the left at the same speed. Ball A is kicked at an angle of 60° above the horizontal, and ball B is kicked at 30° above the horizontal.

(a) Which ball has the larger maximum height?

(b) Which ball takes longer to reach its maximum height?

(c) Which ball lands farther from its starting point?

(d) Which ball takes longer to land?

(e) Which ball has the larger speed when it lands?

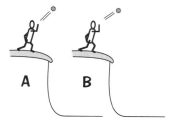

B2. A large rock is catapulted along path A indicated by the dashed line to the right. The path of rock B is not shown, but the location of B when it is at its maximum height is shown with an **x**.

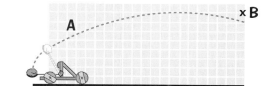

(a) Which rock has the larger maximum height?

(b) Which rock takes longer to reach its maximum height?

(c) Which rock lands farther from the catapult?

(d) Which rock takes longer to land?

(e) Which rock has the larger speed when it lands?

B3. Two balls are thrown from short cliffs as shown. In situation A, the ball is thrown at an angle of 45° above the horizontal. In B, the angle is slightly lower. The balls are thrown at the same speed.

(a) Which ball has the larger maximum height?

(b) Which ball takes longer to reach its maximum height?

(c) Which ball lands farther from the edge of the cliff?

(d) Which ball takes longer to land?

(e) Which ball has the larger speed when it lands?

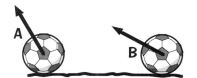

continued

B4. Two balls are thrown from short cliffs as shown. In situation A, the ball is thrown at an angle of about 37° above the horizontal. In B, the angle is about 53° above the horizontal. The balls are thrown at the same speed.

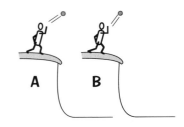

(a) Which ball has the larger maximum height, or are they about the same?

(b) Which ball takes longer to reach its maximum height, or are they about the same?

(c) Which ball lands farther from the edge of the cliff, or are they about the same?

(d) Which ball takes longer to land, or are they about the same?

(e) Which ball has the larger speed when it lands, or are they about the same?

B5. Two balls are thrown from short cliffs as shown. In situation A, the ball is thrown at an angle above the horizontal. In B, the angle is the same, only below the horizontal. The balls are thrown at the same speed.

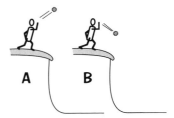

(a) [No question]

(b) [No question]

(c) Which ball lands farther from the edge of the cliff?

(d) Which ball takes longer to land?

(e) Which ball has the larger speed when it lands?

B6. Two balls are thrown from short cliffs as shown. In situation A, the ball is thrown at an angle of 45° above the horizontal. In B, the direction is horizontal, and the initial height is twice as high as in A. The balls are thrown at the same speed. The maximum height of A is the same as the maximum height of B.

(a) [No question; the maximum heights are the same.]

(b) [No question]

(c) Which ball lands farther from the edge of the cliff?

(d) Which ball takes longer to land?

(e) Which ball has the larger speed when it lands?

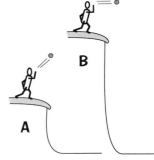

Reflection

R1. (a) In the example for part A, we ignored air resistance. Was this justified? Why?

(b) For which situations in part A did you also ignore air resistance? For which of these is air resistance a significant force? Explain why you think so.

(c) For the situation in which air resistance is most significant, how would your sketches change? Re-draw your sketches showing the effects of air resistance.

R2. (a) For which situations in part B did you <u>not</u> draw a vector diagram for the initial velocity of the projectile, showing the components of the velocity vector? Why not?

(b) For each of these situations, go back and draw the initial velocity vector showing its components, then answer the questions again. Do any of your answers change as a result?

(c) How does a vector diagram for velocity help you answer these questions?

R3. In part B...

(a) ... for which situations did you <u>not</u> sketch velocity and position vs. time? Why not? Did you have difficulty with any of these situations? Explain.

(b) ... for two of the more difficult situations, go back and sketch velocity and position vs. time, then answer the questions again. Do any of your answers change as a result?

(c) How does sketching velocity and/or position vs. time help you answer these questions?

(d) What feature of the velocity vs. time graphs are the same for all the graphs in part B? Why are these all the same?

R4. What principle(s) did you use to answer part (e) of the questions in part B? Explain how you used these principles to compare the final speeds of the projectiles.

R5. Create and describe a situation in which two projectiles have the same initial position and the same initial speed, but one has the larger maximum height and the other has the larger horizontal distance covered before it lands.

Relating Kinematic Quantities for Two-Dimensional Motion

Purpose and Expected Outcome

In this activity you will use the definition of acceleration to derive expressions for velocity vs. time and position vs. time for motion in which the acceleration is constant. You will learn that each component of the motion behaves like one-dimensional motion.

Prior Experience / Knowledge Needed

You need to know the definition of acceleration as the change in velocity per unit time. You should have some experience with algebraic expressions for position and velocity as functions of time in one dimension.

TWO-DIMENSIONAL MOTION

The physical world is three-dimensional, which means that three coordinates are needed to specify the location of something. *Two-dimensional motion* refers to those situations in which only two coordinates (for instance, x and y) are changing as an object or person moves; the third coordinate remains the same. Projectile motion is an example of two-dimension motion. For *one-dimensional motion*, only one coordinate is changing; the other two remain the same, such as when a marble rolls along the floor or a ball is thrown straight up into the air.

Explanation of Activity

There are two parts in this activity. In the first part, you will review how to relate motion quantities for an object moving in one dimension. In the second part, you will write expressions relating motion quantities in two dimensions and use these expressions to answer questions about the motion of objects.

PART A: Analyzing Motion in One Dimension

For each of the situations below, write algebraic expressions for (a) the velocity and (b) the position in terms of the time. In (c), you will be asked to determine some quantities associated with the motion of the object.

A1. A piece of chalk is tossed straight up into the air from an initial height of 1m above the ground. At $t = 1.2$s, the chalk stops at its maximum height and starts to fall down again.

    (a) Write an algebraic expression for the velocity. (Use v_y to represent the velocity.)

    (b) Write an algebraic expression for the position. (Use y to represent the position.)

    (c) – For what time period are your expressions in (a) and (b) valid? Explain.
        – What is the initial velocity of the chalk?
        – What is the final velocity of the chalk?

A2. A car approaches a red traffic light with an initial speed of 45mi/h (about 20m/s) and comes to a stop $3^1/_3$ seconds later. Assume that the car's velocity is positive and that the traffic light is located at the origin.

    (a) Write an expression for the velocity. (Use v_x to represent the velocity.)

    (b) Write an expression for the position. (Use x to represent the position.)

    (c) – For what time period are your expressions in (a) and (b) valid? Explain.
        – What is the car's stopping distance? Explain how you determined this quantity.

A3. A marble is rolling down a very long, but very shallow, inclined plane. At $t = 0$s, the marble is located at the origin. The speed is measured to be about 79cm/s when the marble is located at $x = -150$cm, three seconds later.

    (a) Write an expression for the velocity at all times.

    (b) Write an expression for the position at all times.

    (c) – What is the initial velocity of the marble?
        – When does the marble have this velocity?
        – What is the velocity of the marble at $t = 3$s? Explain.
        – At approximately what time is the marble released from rest? Explain.
        – Where is the marble when it is released from rest? Explain.

A4. A soccer ball is kicked horizontally at 20m/s. After $2^1/_2$ seconds, the ball rolls to a stop.

    (a) Write the velocity as a function of time from $t = 0$s to $t = 5$s. (Use v_x to represent the velocity.)

    (b) Write the position as a function of time from $t = 0$s to $t = 5$s. (Use x to represent the position.)

    (c) – Where is the ball located at $t = 5$s?
        – What is the acceleration of the ball at $t = 5$s?

PART B: Analyzing Motion in Two Dimensions

For each of the situations below, (a) draw a picture of the situation showing the trajectory of the object and an arrow to represent the initial velocity. Then write algebraic expressions for (b) the velocity and (c) the position in terms of the time. In (d), you will be asked to determine some quantities associated with the motion of the object.

B1. A soccer ball is kicked at $37°$ above the horizontal with a speed of 20m/s.

   (a) Draw the path of the soccer ball and an arrow indicating its initial velocity.

   (b) Write algebraic expressions for the x- and y-components of velocity.

   (c) Write algebraic expressions for the x- and y-components of position.

   (d) – What are the x- and y-components of the ball's acceleration?
       – What are the x- and y-components of the initial velocity?
       – When does the soccer ball reach its highest altitude?
       – Where is the soccer ball when it reaches its highest altitude?
       – When does the soccer ball hit the ground?
       – Where is the soccer ball when it hits the ground?

B2. A piece of chalk is thrown across the room from an initial height of 1m above the ground. One and one-third seconds later it lands in a trash can 4m away.

   (a) Draw the path of the chalk and an arrow indicating its initial velocity.

   (b) Write expressions for the velocity.

   (c) Write expressions for the position.

   (d) – What are the x- and y-components of the chalk's initial velocity?
       – When does the chalk reach its highest altitude?
       – Where is the chalk when it reaches its highest altitude?
       – How fast is the chalk moving when it is at its highest altitude?

B3. A toy car rolls up an inclined plane as shown. It stops near the top of the incline at $t = 1.8$s. Be sure to use the given coordinate system throughout.

   (a) Draw the path of the car and arrows to represent its acceleration and initial velocity.

   (b) Write the velocity as a function of time.

   (c) Write the position as a function of time.

   (d) – What are the x- and y-components of the car's initial velocity? Explain.
       – Where is the car located when it reaches its maximum height?
       – What are the x- and y-components of the car's acceleration?
       – What is the car's position and velocity at $t = 2$s? Is this consistent with your expressions and the description above?

Integration of Ideas

Consider the following <u>three</u> situations:

A: a marble is tossed straight up into the air with an initial speed of 8m/s.

B: a marble rolls across the floor with an initial speed of 6m/s. It rolls without any frictional losses.

C: a marble is thrown with an initial speed of 10m/s, with a horizontal component equal to 6m/s and a vertical component equal to 8m/s.

All three marbles start at the (same) origin at the same instant. You will use these three situations throughout this part. Ignore air resistance and use a value of $g = 10$N/kg.

I1. (a) When is marble A at its highest altitude?

(b) Where is marble B when A is at its highest altitude?

(c) When is marble C at its highest altitude?

(d) Where is marble C when it is at its highest altitude?

(e) How fast is marble C moving when it is at its highest altitude?

I2. (a) When does marble A land?

(b) Where is marble B when A lands?

(c) When does marble C land?

(d) Where is marble C when it lands?

I3. Make strobe diagrams for all three marbles, showing their positions at 0.2-second time intervals. Use the same origin, coordinate system and scale for all three diagrams.

I4. (a) What features of the strobe diagrams for A and C are the same? Why?

(b) What features of the strobe diagrams for B and C are the same? Why?

I5. (a) How many expressions in all are needed to write the velocities of all three marbles as functions of time? Explain.

(b) Write expressions for the velocities of all three marbles as functions of time.

(c) Write expressions for the positions of all three marbles as functions of time.

I6. (a) Which expressions above (in I5) are identical?

(b) What does this mean?

Reflection

R1. In part A, for how many situations did you use drawings or sketches to help you answer the questions? Which ones? What kinds of drawings and sketches did you use? Could you have used them more? Would you have been more likely to draw them if you were asked to do it explicitly? Why?

R2. Reconsider situation A2, in which a car is stopping at a traffic light.

(a) Is the initial position of the car positive or negative? Explain. Is this consistent with the description?

(b) What is the direction of the acceleration? Is this direction positive or negative? Is this consistent with your expressions in A2(a) and (b)? Explain.

R3. In one of the situations in part B, both the position and velocity of the object has two components, but the motion is not really "projectile" motion? Which situation is this? Why is it not really projectile motion? (In other words, what is projectile motion?)

R4. Is it possible to write a single expression for the velocity of the toy car in situation B3? Explain how and why. Is it possible to write a single expression for the position of the car? Explain. If possible, write a <u>single</u> expression for the position of the car as a function of time.

R5. In the Integration of Ideas, did you use the answers to I1 and I2 to help you draw the strobe diagrams in I3? Why or why not? Are the strobe diagrams consistent with your answers to I1 and I2? Explain.

R6. In the Integration of Ideas, use your expressions written in I5 to answer the questions in I1 and I2. Which answers are the same? Which answers are different? Which answers are wrong (if any)? Which answers are you more confident of being correct? Why?

Reasoning About Projectile Motion

Purpose and Expected Outcome

In this activity you will reason about the motion of objects undergoing projectile motion. You will learn more about how to relate the initial position and velocity of an object to its maximum height, time of flight, and range. You will also confront some common points of confusion about projectile motion.

Prior Experience / Knowledge Needed

You should have some experience with motion in two dimensions. You should be familiar with the relationships for position and velocity in terms of time, acceleration, initial velocity, and initial position. You should be able to manipulate algebraic expressions.

Explanation of Activity

There are two parts in this activity. In the first part, you will compare six trajectories with each other. In the second part, you will create scenarios to fit given conditions.

PART A: Comparing Trajectories

Shown below are six trajectories, labeled A through F. All six were prepared assuming motion in a gravitational field with no air resistance. The maximum height of A is about 5m. Objects B and C have the same maximum height. Objects E and F also have the same maximum height. Objects B and E land at the same distance from the start, as do objects C and F. Trajectory D has an initial angle of 45°. Use these six trajectories to answer all the questions. Be prepared to discuss your answers with your classmates.

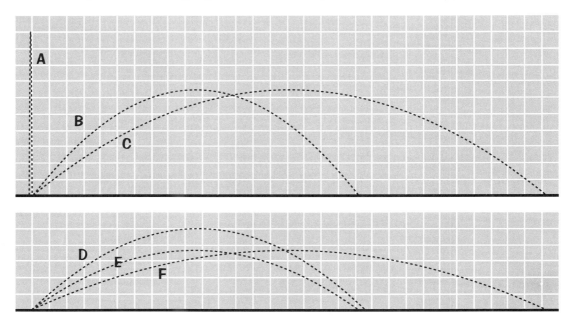

A1. (a) Which object has the larger *x*-component of initial velocity: B or C? E or F?

(b) Which of the six objects has the largest *x*-component of initial velocity?

A2. (a) Which object has the larger *y*-component of initial velocity: B or C? D or E? E or F?

(b) Which of the six objects has the largest *y*-component of initial velocity?

A3. (a) Which object is in the air longer, or are they the same: B or C? E or F? D or E?

(b) Which of the six objects is in the air the longest?

A4. (a) Which object has the larger initial speed, or are they the same: A or B? C or F?

(b) Which has the larger initial speed: B or C? B or E? E or F?

A5. (a) Which object most likely has an initial velocity of (6m/s, 8m/s)? Explain why you think so.

(b) Which object most likely has an initial velocity of (7m/s, 7m/s)? Explain why you think so.

Summary of Part A

Three quantities are particularly relevant for identifying, distinguishing, and analyzing trajectories: *range*, *maximum altitude*, and *time of flight*. The range is the horizontal distance traveled by the projectile from the time it is fired until it lands. The maximum altitude is the height of the highest point in the trajectory. The time of flight is the amount of time the projectile spends in the air between when it is fired and when it lands.

In the next part we will examine these three quantities and learn how they can be used to analyze situations.

PART B: Creating and Analyzing Scenarios

B1. If two projectiles have the same *range*, <u>must</u> they have the same initial speed? Explain. If not, create a situation in which two objects travel the same horizontal distance, but they have different initial speeds.

B2. If the *maximum altitudes* of two projectiles are the same, <u>must</u> they have the same initial speed? Explain. If not, create a situation in which two objects have the same maximum height but different initial speeds.

B3. If two projectiles have the same range, <u>must</u> they have the same time of flight? Explain. If not, create a situation in which two objects cover the same horizontal distance, but they spend different amounts of time in the air.

B4. Two people are standing on the edge of a cliff. One throws a ball straight up, and the other throws an identical ball straight down. The initial speeds of the two balls are the same.

(a) Which ball will have the larger speed when it lands? Explain.

(b) Which ball will have the larger <u>average</u> speed for the time interval it is in the air? Explain.

B5. Two projectiles have the same initial speed and spend the same amount of time in the air. What other features of their trajectories must be the same also? Explain.

B6. Create a situation in which the initial positions, initial speeds and the ranges of two projectiles are the same, but the maximum altitudes are different. What else about the two trajectories is different?

Reflection

R1. Does a large range mean that the projectile is in the air a long time? Explain why or why not. If possible, give an example of a situation in which the range is large, but the projectile does not spend very much time in the air.

R2. Does a large maximum altitude mean that the projectile is in the air a long time? Explain why or why not.   If possible, give an example of a situation in which the maximum height is large, but the projectile does not spend very much time in the air.

R3. Does a large maximum height mean that the projectile also has a large range? Explain why or why not. If possible, give an example of a situation in which the maximum height is large, but the projectile does not have a very large range.

R4. What kinds of drawings and sketches did you use to help answer the questions in part B? Which were the most helpful?

R5. How far away from its initial position does an object land when it has an initial velocity of (10m/s, 0m/s)? Explain.

Solving Problems in Projectile Motion

Purpose and Expected Outcome

In this activity you will solve problems involving objects undergoing projectile motion. You will learn how to analyze situations using either initial conditions or general features of trajectories. You will also learn how to use algebraic expressions for the position and velocity of a projectile.

Prior Experience / Knowledge Needed

You should be familiar with expressions for the position and velocity of a projectile in terms of initial conditions (i.e., initial position and initial velocity), acceleration, and time. You should be familiar with the main features of a trajectory, namely *time of flight*, *maximum height* and *range*. You should understand the relationships between initial conditions and the features of a trajectory.

You also need to know the main principles of mechanics and how to use them to solve problems, namely Newton's laws, and Conservation of Momentum and Energy.

FREE-FALL ACCELERATION

An object in *free-fall* has only one force on it: gravitation, $F_g = mg$, where $g \approx 10\text{N/kg}$ is the gravitational constant. According to Newton's 2nd law, this means that all objects in free-fall have the same acceleration, $a_g \approx 10\text{m/s}^2$. Even though a_g and g have the same units ($1\text{N/kg} = 1\text{m/s}^2$) and the same numerical value (≈ 10), g is not an acceleration; it is a proportionality constant in an empirical force law, and its units (N/kg) remind us of this. All objects (near the Earth) have a force of gravitation on them equal to mg, but only objects in free-fall have an acceleration equal to a_g. We notate this special acceleration as a_g to remind us that it is an acceleration and that it corresponds to a situation in which the only force on the object is gravitation. We generally use a value of $a_g \approx 10\text{m/s}^2$ when analyzing situations and solving problems.

Explanation of Activity

There are two parts in this activity. In the first part, you will use your knowledge of projectile motion and the principles of mechanics to solve some problems. The second part is a hands-on activity in which you will predict where a projectile will land when shot from a rubber-band sling shot.

PART A: Solving Problems in Simple Projectile Motion

In this part, you will solve some projectile motion problems in which air resistance is ignored. You should assume that the initial velocity is denoted (v_{0x}, v_{0y}), and that the acceleration is constant and equal to $a_g \approx 10\text{m/s}^2$.

A1. A baseball is thrown as shown with an initial velocity of (8m/s, 6m/s).

    (a) What is the smallest speed of the baseball, and where does this occur?

    (b) How long does it take before the ball lands?

    (c) Write a general expression for this time using known or given quantities, such as v_{0x} and v_{0y}. (This is the *time of flight T*.)

A2. A baseball is thrown off a cliff as shown, with an initial velocity of (6m/s, 8m/s). It lands with a speed of 14m/s.

    (a) What is the initial height of the ball above the ground? (**Hint:** Use energy ideas.)

    (b) How long does it take before the ball lands?

    (c) Where does the ball land relative to the base of the cliff?

A3. A baseball is thrown as shown with an initial velocity of (8m/s, 6m/s).

    (a) What is the maximum height of the ball?

    (b) Write a general expression for this height using known or given quantities, such as v_{0x} and v_{0y}. (This is the *maximum altitude H*.)

A4. A baseball is thrown off a cliff as shown, with an initial velocity of (3m/s, 4m/s), from a height of 5m above level ground.

    (a) When does the ball land?

    (b) How fast is the ball moving when it lands?

    (c) Where does the ball land relative to the base of the cliff?

PART B: Predicting Where a Projectile Will Land

This is a hands-on activity. The goal is to use your knowledge of Newton's laws, energy conservation, and projectile motion to predict where a marble will land when shot from a rubber-band sling shot.

B1. **Finding the spring constant for the sling shot.**

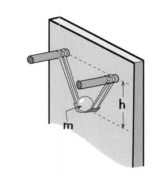

Your teacher will give you a set of data showing the relationship between the height h and the mass m when the sling shot is held vertically as shown, and different masses are put into it. Note that height h is measured from the middle of the posts to the bottom of the mass.

Use this data to estimate the spring constant for the sling shot.

B2. **Finding the initial speed of the marble.**

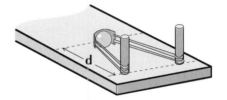

In order to predict the trajectory of the marble, you need to determine the initial speed of the marble after it leaves the sling shot. Your teacher will tell you how far the sling shot will be stretched (d) before firing the marble horizontally.

Use your results from B1 above to estimate the initial speed of the marble.

B3. **Predicting where the marble will land.**

Use your results from B1 and B2 to compute where the marble will land when it is shot horizontally off the edge of a table. Put a piece of tape on the floor, with your team's name on it and an **x** to show where you think the marble will land.

B4. **Testing your prediction.**

Your teacher will fire the marble 10 times. Record the location of each landing, and make a visual record of the results. (For example, make a scatter plot showing the locations of the landings.) Estimate the average value of the location, and estimate how large a circle around this average value contains about 2/3 of the results. (The size of this circle is an estimate of how narrow or spread out the data are.)

How close was your team's prediction? Explain any discrepancies.

Reflection

R1. If you double the vertical component of velocity (but keep the horizontal component the same), what features of the trajectory are affected? By what factor? Explain.

R2. If you double the horizontal component of velocity (but keep the vertical component the same), what features of the trajectory are affected? By what factor? Explain.

R3. For B1, B2, and B3, indicate the principle(s) used to solve each problem. For example, what principle(s) did you use to estimate the spring constant for the sling shot in problem B1?

R4. What sketches or drawings were helpful for answering the questions in part B?

R5. For at least one of the questions in part B, a sketch is essential for answering the question. Which question(s)? What kind of sketch did you use? How was the sketch used to answer the question(s)?

Solving Problems in Two-Dimensional Motion

Purpose and Expected Outcome

In this activity you will solve problems involving objects undergoing two-dimensional motion. You will learn that solving problems in two dimensions is not very different from solving problems in projectile motion.

Prior Experience / Knowledge Needed

You should be familiar with expressions for the position and velocity of a projectile in terms of initial conditions (i.e., initial position and initial velocity), acceleration, and time. You should be familiar with the main features of a trajectory, namely *time of flight*, *maximum height* and *range*. You should understand the relationships between initial conditions and the features of a trajectory.

You also need to know the main principles of mechanics and how to use them to solve problems, namely Newton's laws, and Conservation of Momentum and Energy.

GENERAL EXPRESSIONS FOR CONSTANT ACCELERATION

When the acceleration of an object is constant, we can write general algebraic expressions for the position and velocity of the object as functions of time.

$$x(t) = x_0 + v_{0x}t + \frac{1}{2}a_x t^2 \qquad y(t) = y_0 + v_{0y}t + \frac{1}{2}a_y t^2$$
$$v_x(t) = v_{0x} + a_x t \qquad v_y(t) = v_{0y} + a_y t$$

where x and y refer to two coordinates of the position of the object. The initial position is denoted (x_0, y_0), and the initial velocity is (v_{0x}, v_{0y}). The acceleration is constant and equal to (a_x, a_y). When the acceleration is equal to $(0, -a_g)$, we get simple projectile motion.

Explanation of Activity

Below are four problems involving two-dimensional motion but also involving other useful principles and ideas.

A1. A large inclined plane is positioned on a table as shown, at an angle of 30° relative to the horizontal. A frictionless puck is launched from one corner of the plane at 25cm/s, maintaining contact with the plane during its entire trajectory. The initial velocity of the puck makes an angle of 53° with the bottom of the plane.

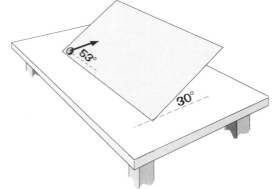

  (a) What is the acceleration of the puck?

  (b) What are the components of the initial velocity of the puck?

  (c) What is the maximum height of the puck above the horizontal surface?

  (d) Where does the puck return to the horizontal surface? When does this happen?

A2. A spring-loaded gun shoots a small pellet at an initial speed of about 20m/s. You take the gun onto an open elevator (such as those on construction sites) and start rising at 5m/s. If you fire the gun horizontally three seconds later, where will the pellet land?

A3. An explosive device is shot straight up into the air. When the device reaches its maximum altitude, it explodes into two equal-mass pieces. One piece lands 20m from the launch site 2 seconds after the explosion, and the other lands 40m from the site.

  (a) What are the final velocities of the two pieces?

  (b) What is the initial speed of the explosive device?

  (c) How long does the entire process take?

A4. A small catapult throws a rock along the trajectory shown in the strobe diagram below. The time between strobes is about $^1/_3$ s.

  (a) Write expressions for the position and velocity of the rock as functions of time. Be as quantitative as possible.

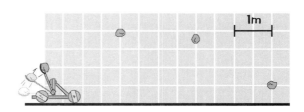

  (b) When does the rock hit the ground?

  (c) What is the maximum height of the rock above the ground? When does this occur?

  (d) If the rock weighs 350N, estimate the amount of energy stored in the catapult before firing it.

Reflection

R1. For each of the four problems, indicate the major principle (other than projectile motion) you used to solve the problem.

R2. (a) What sketches or drawings did you use to help you solve these problems? Explain how they helped you.

(b) What sketches or drawings did your classmates use that you did not use? What are some reasons why you did not use them? Do you need to learn better how to use them?

R3. For question A4(d), you estimated the initial energy stored in the catapult before it was fired. Was this estimate a lower limit or upper limit on the amount of stored energy? Explain. What factors are not included in your estimate? Explain why they are not included.

AT·12

Exploring Ideas About Relative Motion

Purpose and Expected Outcome

In this activity, you will begin studying relative motion more formally than you have until now. You already know all the concepts about the motion of objects and their interactions with the world. You need to review what you have learned so far, and learn how to apply concepts to more complicated situations.

Prior Experience / Knowledge Needed

You need to know basic motion concepts, such as *velocity* and *position*. You should have some experience sketching, interpreting, and analyzing graphs of position vs. time.

Explanation of Activity and Example

For each of the following situations, (a) draw a picture showing the initial positions of all the objects and people in the situation. Then, draw sketches of position vs. time for each of the objects or people (b) from one point of view, and (c) from a second point of view. In some cases, (d) you will be asked to answer a question about the situation. Assume that the "positive" direction is "to the right". Be prepared to explain your answers.

E1. You are sitting on some steps watching a bus go by. In particular, your friend Jamie is sitting in the back seat and you wave to him as he passes by.

   (a) Draw the physical situation, showing the relative positions of you, Jamie and the bus driver at $t = 0s$.

   (b) From <u>your</u> point of view, sketch the position vs. time for you, Jamie, and the bus driver. Assume you are at the origin of your coordinate system.

   (c) Sketch the position vs. time for you, Jamie, and the bus driver, this time from Jamie's point of view. (Assume Jamie is at the origin of his coordinate system.)

Answers: *Answers are shown to the right.*

Explanations: *We assume that the bus is moving to your right and that initially the entire bus is to your left. This means that initially the bus driver has a negative position, and that Jamie has an even larger negative position. The bus driver and Jamie are moving with the same positive velocity, so the slopes of their position vs. time graphs are the same. You are at rest at the origin, so your position vs. time graph is horizontal and equal to zero at all times.*

   From Jamie's point of view, he is at rest at the origin, so his position vs. time graph is horizontal and equal to zero at all times. The bus driver is a fixed distance in front of Jamie, so his graph is horizontal also. You are moving in the negative direction, starting at a positive position in front of both Jamie and the bus driver. Note that the time at which you and Jamie pass each other is the same from both points of view.

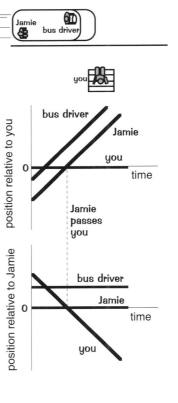

continued

A1. You are sitting on some steps watching a bus go by. In particular, your friend Jamie is in the back of the bus walking toward the front. You wave to him as he passes by.

(a) Make a drawing showing the relative positions of you, Jamie, and the bus driver at $t = 0$s.

(b) From your point of view, sketch the position vs. time for you, Jamie, and the bus driver. Assume you are at the origin.

(c) Sketch the position vs. time for you, Jamie, and the bus driver, this time from the bus driver's point of view. (Assume the bus driver is at the origin of her coordinate system.)

A2. You are sitting on some steps watching a bus go by at 5mi/h. Your friend Betty is near the front of the bus running toward the back at 5mi/h.

(a) Make a drawing of this situation at $t = 0$s.

(b) From your point of view, sketch the position vs. time for you and Betty.

(c) Sketch the position vs. time for you and Betty, this time from the bus driver's point of view.

(d) How fast is Betty moving relative to you? Explain how this is possible.

A3. You are running at 7mi/h towards some steps, beside a bus moving in the same direction at 5mi/h. Your friend Charlie is on the bus, walking toward the front of the bus at 2mi/h.

(a) Make a drawing of this situation at $t = 0$s.

(b) From the point of view of the ground, sketch the position vs. time for you and Charlie, assuming the steps are at the origin.

(c) Sketch the position vs. time for you and Charlie, this time from Charlie's point of view.

(d) How fast is Charlie moving relative to the ground? Explain. How fast is Charlie moving relative to you? Explain.

A4. You are running at 7mi/h, beside a bus moving in the opposite direction at 5mi/h. Your friend Charlie is on the bus, walking toward the front of the bus at 2mi/h. After you and the bus pass by each other, you run past a set of steps.

(a) Make a drawing of this situation at $t = 0$s.

(b) From the point of view of someone standing on the ground, sketch the position vs. time for you and Charlie, assuming the steps are at the origin.

(c) Sketch the position vs. time for you and Charlie, this time from the bus driver's point of view. Use the <u>back</u> of the bus as the origin.

(d) What is your <u>velocity</u> relative to the bus driver? Explain. What is Charlie's velocity relative to you? Explain.

Reflection

R1. Have you ever been in a car (or bus, train, or airplane) that is stopped when a car (or another vehicle) beside you starts to move? If so, describe the sensation. Did you think that you were moving instead of the vehicle beside you? In what direction? How did you determine eventually that you were still at rest and the other vehicle was moving instead?

R2. What does the phrase *at rest* mean to you? What does the term *moving* mean to you? When a person is sitting "at rest" in a "moving" car, is the person moving or not? When you are sitting "at rest" in your seat, are you moving relative to the Sun? Are you moving relative to the center of the Earth?

R3. Do the laws of physics (for instance, Newton's 2nd law) appear to remain valid when you are in a moving vehicle, such as a car, train, or airplane? Explain. Under what circumstances do you suppose the laws of physics are not valid? Explain. Give an example of a situation in which the laws of physics are definitely not valid.

R4. Create and describe a situation in which you are on a moving bus, but you are at rest relative to the ground. What is the relationship between the velocity of the bus (relative to the ground) and your velocity relative to the bus?

R5. Create and describe a situation in which you are on a bus that is moving in the positive direction (relative to the ground), but you are moving in the negative direction relative to the ground. What must be true about the speed of the bus compared to your speed in the bus?

R6. If a vehicle (such as a bus or train) has a velocity v_1 relative to the ground, and you have a velocity v_2' relative to the vehicle, what is your velocity v_2 relative to the ground? Does this relationship remain true when one of the velocities is negative? Explain.

R7. If you have a position x_1' relative to another person, who has a position x_2 relative to the ground, what is your position x_1 relative to the ground? Does this relationship remain true when one of the positions is negative? Explain.

Exploring Relative Motion in One and Two Dimensions

Purpose and Expected Outcome

In this activity you will learn how to adapt relative motion ideas developed in one dimension to motion in two dimensions.

Prior Experience / Knowledge Needed

You need to know how to add vectors, both algebraically and pictorially. You should have some experience with relative motion in one dimension.

REFERENCE FRAMES

A *reference frame* is an origin and a set of coordinate axes (e.g., x, y and z). One reference frame can be moving relative to another reference frame, as shown below. Frame O is on the ground in front of a moving train, and its horizontal axis is labeled x. Another frame O' is on the train, and its horizontal axis is labeled x'. Frame O' is moving with velocity u (relative to O) because the train is moving with velocity u relative to the ground. Also, frame O is moving with velocity $-u$ as seen from O', because the ground is moving past the train at velocity $-u$.

Positions can be measured relative to either reference frame. So, for instance, the position of the ball is $x'_{BALL} = 3m$ in O', but $x_{BALL} = 1m$ in O. (Note that the first position is "primed" and the second is "unprimed".) These positions are different because the origin of O' is not

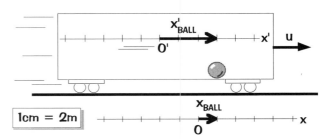

lined up with the origin of O. In general, $x' = x'_O + x$, where x'_O is the location of the origin of O as measured in O'. (That is, $x'_O = 2m$ at the instant shown.)

Similarly, to convert positions from O' to O, we use the location of the origin of O' as measured in O, $x_{O'} = -2m$. So, $x = x_{O'} + x'$. For the ball, $x_{BALL} = -2m + 3m = 1m$.

Explanation of Activity

There are two parts in this activity. In the first part, you will review how to relate motion quantities for an object moving in one dimension. In the second part, you will extend your ideas to two dimensions.

PART A: Analyzing Motion in One Dimension

In all of the situations below, assume that all motion is along a single direction.

A1. A large cruise ship is crossing from New York, USA to Lisbon, Portugal at 22mi/h (about 10m/s). A passenger hits a golf ball off the back of the ship at 90mi/h (about 40m/s). How fast does the golf ball travel relative to the water?

A2. Abigail is swimming upstream at $2^{1}/_{4}$mi/h (about 1m/s). To someone on a bridge, she appears to be going downstream at 4mi/h (about 1.8m/s). How fast is the water moving?

A3. An airplane is flying at 250mi/h at 12,000ft above the ground. An airline attendant rolls a cart of sodas toward the front of the airplane at 2mi/h.
(a) What is the velocity of the cart as measured from the ground?
(b) Why is it so difficult to tell how fast you are going when you are inside an airplane?

A4. An airplane is flying at 350mi/h (relative to the air) into a steady wind moving at 60mi/h.
(a) How fast is the plane flying relative to the ground?
(b) Why is it easier to take off in a plane going into the wind rather than with the wind?

Summary of part A

Let's go back to the situation on the previous page, and assume now that the ball is rolling toward the back of the train. Its velocity is measured to be $v'_{BALL} = -4$m/s relative to the train, and the train is moving at velocity $u = 6$m/s relative to the ground.

When two frames are moving relative to each other, velocity is different when measured in the two frames. In this case, the ball would appear to be moving at $v_{BALL} = 2$m/s as seen from the ground (i.e., to the <u>right</u>). The velocity as measured in O is related to the velocity as measured in

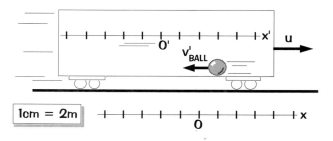

O' according to $v = v_{O'} + v'$, where $v_{O'}$ is the velocity of frame O' as measured in O. (In this case, $v_{O'} = u = 6$m/s.) Similarly, $v' = v'_O + v$, where $v'_O = -u = -6$m/s is the velocity of frame O as measured in O'.

PART B: Analyzing Motion in Two Dimensions

In each of the situations below, there are two well defined reference frames moving relative to each other. One is the Earth (or the ground), which we label O. The other frame is labeled O'. For each situation, (a) draw a picture showing the path followed by the object (or person) as seen in frame O and arrows to represent the velocity of frame O' and the velocity of the object relative to that frame. Then (b) indicate the velocity of the object as seen in frame O, and (c) answer questions about the situation.

B1. Starting at the ✘, a boy swims at 1m/s across a 200m-wide river moving at 0.6m/s.

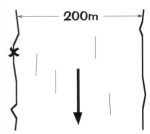

(a) Draw the boy, showing the direction he is facing just after he starts to swim. Then draw his path and an arrow to indicate his velocity relative to the water. (An arrow for the velocity of the water as seen from the far bank is shown. Use the same scale for the boy's velocity relative to the water.)

(b) What is the velocity of the boy as seen by an observer on the far bank?

(c) – What direction is the boy facing when he is swimming?
– How long does it take for the boy to reach the other side of the river?
– How far does the boy think he swims to reach the other side of the river?

B2. A cannon fires a ball at 15m/s. The cannon is mounted on a railroad car, pointed at an angle of 53° above the horizontal as shown, and pulled at a constant speed of 10m/s.

(a) Draw the path of the ball and arrows to represent the velocity of the railroad car as seen from the ground and the initial velocity of the ball relative to the railroad car.

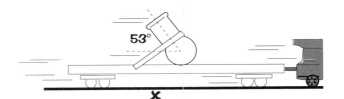

(b) What is the initial velocity of the ball relative to the ground?

(c) – What is the initial speed of the ball relative to the ground?
– Where does the ball land relative to the ✘ in the diagram above?
– How far apart are the ball and cannon when the ball lands?

B3. A small airplane is traveling west at 120mi/h as determined by radar on the ground. A steady wind is measured to be about 40mi/h directed north.

(a) Draw the airplane, showing the direction it is facing while flying. Then draw the path the plane is following, and arrows to represent its velocity relative to the air and the velocity of the air relative to the ground.

(b) What is the velocity of the airplane relative to the ground?

(c) – What is the velocity of the airplane relative to the air?
– What direction is the airplane facing?

Reflection

R1. In part A, did you use any drawings or sketches to help you answer the questions? Why or why not? What kinds of drawings or sketches did you use? How did they help?

R2. Is it possible to swim in a river so that you are always directly underneath a bridge over the river? Explain why or why not. If it is possible, describe how you would do it.

R3. Reconsider situation B1, in which a boy swims across a river. Is it possible for him to get across the river even sooner, perhaps by swimming at an angle (relative to the water)? Explain why or why not. If it is possible, in what direction should he swim?

R4. Reconsider situation B2, in which a cannon ball is fired from a rolling railroad car.
   (a) Is there a velocity you could choose for the railroad car that would cause the cannon ball to go straight up into the air? Explain. If it is possible, what should be the chosen velocity of the railroad car?
   (b) Is there a velocity you could choose for the railroad car that would cause the cannon ball to go towards the right rather than the left? Explain. What must be true about the velocity of the railroad car for the cannon ball to land to the right of the ✘?
   (c) How does the time at which the cannon ball lands depend on the speed of the railroad car? Explain.

R5. Reconsider situation B3, in which a small airplane is flying in the wind.
   (a) After 40 minutes how far has the airplane traveled relative to the ground?
   (b) After 40 minutes how far has the airplane traveled relative to the air?
   (c) Which value for the distance above should you use to estimate the amount of fuel needed for the trip? Explain.

R6. Is it possible for an airplane to fly facing west (for 4 hours, let's say) and land east of where it took off? Explain why or why not. If it is possible, describe a way for this to happen.

Reasoning About Relative Motion

Purpose and Expected Outcome

In this activity you will reason about the motion of objects in moving frames. You will learn more about how to relate the position and velocity of an object in one frame to its position and velocity in another frame.

Prior Experience / Knowledge Needed

You should have some experience with motion in one and two dimensions. You should be familiar with relative motion in one and two dimensions. Also, you should be familiar with the Impulse–Momentum Theorem and Conservation of Energy, and you should know how to find the work done on an object by a force. Finally, you should be familiar with projectile motion.

Explanation of Activity

In each of the situations described below, you are asked to reason out an answer. Try not to get too bogged down with numerical values.

SITUATION A: Throwing Balls

Two boys throw identical 250g balls horizontally at 10m/s. Boy A is inside a railroad car traveling at a constant speed of 20m/s as seen from the ground, and the other (B) is outside the railroad car standing on the ground.

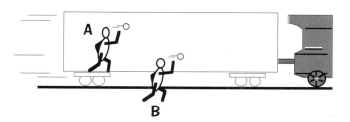

A1. Which boy exerts the larger average force on the ball while throwing it? Explain.

A2. Which boy delivers the larger impulse to the ball while throwing it? Explain.

A3. Which **ball** has more work done on it during the throw? Explain.

A4. Which boy converts more of his internal energy into kinetic energy of the ball? Explain.

A5. Are your answers to A2 and A3 consistent with each other? Are your answers to A3 and A4 consistent with each other? Explain any apparent contradictions.

SITUATION B: Swimming Across a River

Two girls (Arielle and Bebe) are attempting to swim across a slowly flowing river. They both begin at the ✖ and swim at the same speed (relative to the water) but in different directions. Their velocities relative to the water are shown at right. The velocity of the water relative to the ground is also shown.

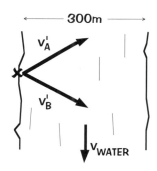

B1. Which girl reaches the other side first? Explain.

B2. Which girl has the larger speed relative to the ground? Explain.

B3. Which girl travels the longer distance before reaching the other side? Explain.

B4. Which girl do you suppose is more tired when she reaches the other side? Explain.

B5. Are your answers to B1 and B2 consistent with each other? Explain any apparent contradictions.

SITUATION C: Firing Cannons Mounted On Railroad Cars

Two identical cannons that fire cannon balls at 35m/s are mounted onto two railroad cars as shown. Railroad car A is pulled at a constant speed of 8m/s to the right, while railroad car B is pulled at a constant speed of 8m/s to the left. Both cannons are fired when they reach the **✗**'s in the diagram below.

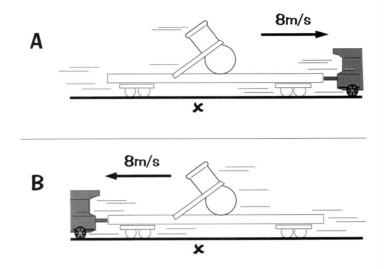

C1. As measured from the ground, which ball has the larger initial speed, or are they the same? Explain.

C2. Which ball reaches a larger maximum height? Explain.

C3. Which ball lands farther from its **✗**? Explain.

C4. Which ball lands farther from its railroad car? Explain.

C5. Which ball has more kinetic energy immediately after being fired? Explain.

C6. Which cannon gives more energy to the ball when it is fired? Explain.

C7. Are your answers to C5 and C6 consistent with each other? Explain any apparent contradictions.

Reflection

R1. Create and describe a situation in which the vertical components of the velocity are different in two different frames, but the horizontal components are the same. What <u>must</u> be true about the relative velocity of the two frames?

R2. (a) Which answers in this activity seem to depend on the frame of reference? For instance, reconsider C5. Does the amount of kinetic energy depend on the frame?

(b) Which answers seem to not depend on the frame?

R3. Are the laws of physics valid on the Earth? Explain. Are the laws valid in a frame moving relative to the Earth? Explain. Under what circumstances do you suppose the laws of physics might not be valid? Explain. Give an example of a situation in which the laws of physics (as you have learned them) do not appear to be valid.

R4. (a) Estimate the speed of the Earth relative to the Sun.

(b) Estimate the speed of a person standing at the equator relative to the center of the Earth.

(c) Estimate the acceleration of a person standing at the equator relative to the center of the Earth.

(d) Comment on the validity of experiments done on the Earth to verify or demonstrate the laws of physics.

R5. (a) Which types of relative motion are hardest for you to visualize? For each type listed below, rate its difficulty from 1–10, where 1 is easiest to visualize and 10 is hardest.

       i. someone moving on a boat

      ii. something thrown on a boat

     iii. someone swimming in a flowing river

     iv. someone moving on a bus

      v. something moving on a bus

     vi. someone moving on a railroad car

    vii. something moving on a railroad car

   viii. someone moving on an airplane

     ix. something moving on an airplane

      x. an airplane flying in windy air

     xi. a ball fired from a cannon mounted on a railroad car

(b) Why do you suppose the hard ones are hard for you? What makes the easy ones easy for you?

Solving Problems in Relative Motion

Purpose and Expected Outcome

In this activity you will solve problems involving frames moving relative to each other.

Prior Experience / Knowledge Needed

You should be familiar with relative motion. You need to know the main principles of mechanics and how to use them to solve problems, namely Newton's laws, Conservation of Momentum and Conservation of Energy.

ADDING VELOCITIES

Imagine a bus moving to the right as shown below. Inside the bus, three items are moving: (1) Arlo is walking toward the front of the bus; (2) a ball is being thrown at an angle inside the bus; and (3) a second ball is being thrown out of a window.

The velocities as seen from the bus are shown with a "prime" (e.g., v'_{ARLO} and v'_{BALL1}), and the velocities as seen from the ground are shown as "unprimed" (v_{ARLO} and v_{BALL1}). Mathematically, we can see that vector addition relates the velocities as seen from different frames:

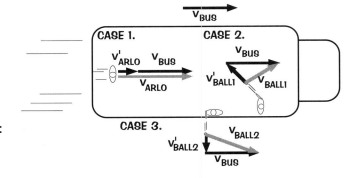

$$\mathbf{v} = \mathbf{v}' + \mathbf{v}_{BUS}$$

In other words, the velocity as seen from the ground ($\mathbf{v}$) is equal to the vector sum of the velocity as seen from the bus ($\mathbf{v}'$) and the velocity of the bus as seen from the ground ($\mathbf{v}_{BUS}$). This is true in one, two, and three dimensions. Note that $\mathbf{v}_{BUS}$ is actually the velocity of the "primed" frame as seen from the "unprimed" frame.

Explanation of Activity

Below are four problems involving relative motion but also involving other useful principles and ideas. Be prepared to discuss your answers with your classmates.

A1. On a flight from Detroit to Grand Rapids, the wind is measured to be going 45mi/h (20m/s) with gusts up to 65mi/h (29m/s) as seen from the ground. The wind is coming from the northeast.

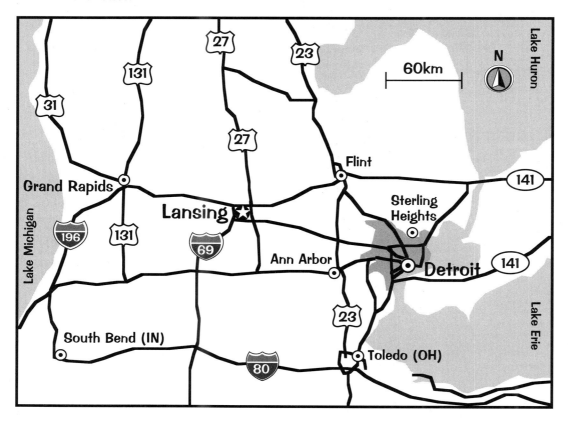

(a) If the airplane cruises at 180mi/h (80m/s) in still air, what direction should the pilot point the airplane?

(b) Approximately how long will it take for the plane to reach Grand Rapids?

(c) On the return flight to Detroit, what direction should the pilot point the airplane?

(d) How long will it take for the plane to return to Detroit?

(e) Are your answers to (b) and (d) consistent with each other? Explain any apparent contradictions.

continued

A2. Betty is attempting to cross a river. The river flows at 1.8km/h (¹/₂m/s) and Betty can swim at 2.4km/h (²/₃m/s). Betty's path is shown in the diagram at right.

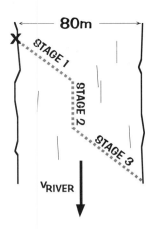

(a) What is the scale used in the diagram for velocity?

(b) What is the scale used in the diagram for distance?

(c) What direction is Betty swimming relative to the water? Explain.

(d) What might stage 2 of Betty's path represent? Approximately how much time passes during stage 2?

(e) How long does it take Betty to cross the river?

A3. Charlie throws a 145g baseball horizontally from inside a train as shown. The train is moving at 16m/s, and Charlie throws the ball at 10m/s relative to the train.

(a) What is the impulse delivered to the baseball?

(b) As determined by an observer on the ground, what is the change in kinetic energy of the baseball? What is the total work done on the baseball?

(c) Imagine that the ball is thrown in the same manner by someone on the ground. Which answers above would be the same? Which would be different?

(d) Does it require more, less, or the same amount of effort by Charlie to throw the baseball when on the train compared to when on the ground? Explain.

(e) To an observer on the ground, where does the extra energy come from to give to the baseball when it is thrown on the train?

A4. Charlie throws a 145g baseball horizontally from inside a train as shown. The train is moving at 16m/s, and Charlie throws the ball at 10m/s relative to the train.

(a) What is the impulse delivered to the baseball?

(b) As determined by an observer on the ground, what is the change in kinetic energy of the baseball? What is the total work done on the baseball?

(c) Does it require more, less, or the same amount of effort for Charlie to throw the baseball in this situation compared to the situation above (in A3)? Explain.

(d) How is it that Charlie seems to be expending energy, yet to someone standing on the ground, the kinetic energy of the ball is getting smaller? Explain.

Reflection

R1. What physical principles did you use to solve these problems? On which parts of which problems did you use each principle?

R2. (a) What sketches or drawings did you use to help you solve these problems? Explain how they helped you.

  (b) What sketches or drawings did your classmates use that you did not use? What are some reasons why you did not use them? Do you need to learn better how to use them?

R3. (a) What physical quantities are the same when viewed from two frames moving relative to each other? For example, is a force exerted on an object the same in both frames? Is the acceleration of an object the same in both frames?

  (b) Does your answer in (a) depend on the relative velocity of the two frames? Explain. Does it depend on the relative acceleration of the two frames? Explain.

R4. (a) What physical quantities are different when viewed from two frames moving relative to each other? For example, is a force exerted on an object different in the two frames? Is the acceleration of an object different in the two frames?

  (b) Does your answer in (a) depend on the relative velocity of the two frames? Explain. Does it depend on the relative acceleration of the two frames? Explain.

R5. Reconsider situation A3, in which Charlie throws a baseball while inside a moving train.

  (a) How would the path of the baseball compare to the path of a second baseball thrown from the ground at 26m/s?

  (b) Which ball would hit the ground first? Explain.

R6. Annette and Barb are holding identical ping pong balls from the same height above their feet. Assuming the two balls are released at the same instant...

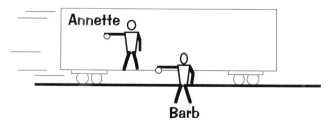

  (a) ... which ball will land first, or will they land at the same time? Explain.

  (b) If air resistance is <u>not</u> ignored, which ball will land first? Explain.

Graphing Rotational Motion

Purpose and Expected Outcome

This series of activities will study rotational motion in analogy with linear motion. In this activity, you will become familiar with some rotational motion quantities, such as *angular position*, *angular velocity*, and *angular acceleration*. You will discover that you already have learned some rotational motion ideas, though perhaps without realizing it. You will learn that rotational quantities are *analogous* to linear quantities, such as position, velocity, and acceleration. Also, you will see that many properties of rotational ideas are similar to their linear counterparts.

Prior Experience / Knowledge Needed

You should understand linear motion ideas, such as *position*, *velocity*, and *acceleration*. You should know how to sketch graphs of position, velocity, and acceleration vs. time, and you should know the relationships among position, velocity, and acceleration. You should know that there are 360° or 2π radians in a circle.

ROTATIONAL MOTION QUANTITIES

Each linear motion quantity has a corresponding rotational motion counterpart. *Angular position* is the angle θ made by an object or arrangement relative to some chosen reference, such as the vertical or horizontal. In the diagram at right, the angle θ ("theta") is measured counterclockwise from the table top, and at the instant shown, θ = 72°. *Angular velocity* is the rate ω ("omega") at which the angle θ is changing. In the example, ω is negative, because θ is positive and getting smaller. *Angular acceleration* is the rate α ("alpha") at which the angular velocity ω is changing. (In the example, we have no information about how the angular velocity is changing.)

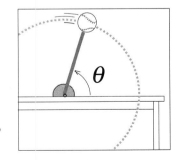

Explanation of Activity

Identify the object(s) that correspond to the given graph. Use following seven objects throughout this part. They are described below.

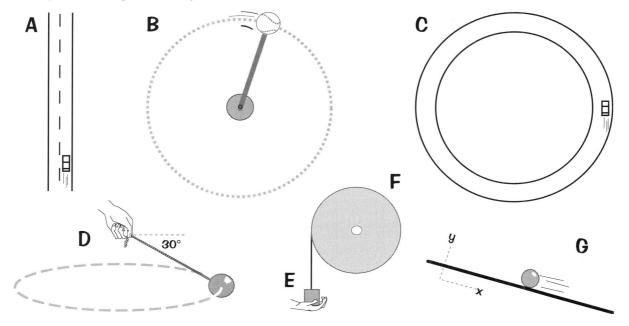

Object A: a **car** drives down a long, straight highway at constant speed.

Object B: a **baseball** is attached to a light rod, which spins at a constant rate using a motor attached to the pivot.

Object C: a **car** drives around a circular track at constant speed.

Object D: a **ball** swings in a horizontal circle.

Objects E & F: a **block** is attached to a string wound around a solid **wheel** and released from rest. The wheel spins around a fixed axle.

Object G: a **marble** rolls up a shallow incline.

A1. (a) Which of the objects above might have the angular position (θ) vs. time plot to the right? Explain.

(b) Which of the objects above might have the position (x) vs. time plot to the right? Explain.

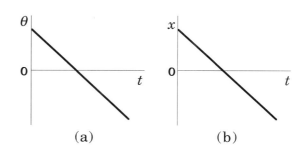

(a)   (b)

continued

A2. (a) Which of the objects might have the angular position (θ) vs. time plot to the right? Explain.

(b) Which of the objects might have the position (x) vs. time plot to the right? Explain.

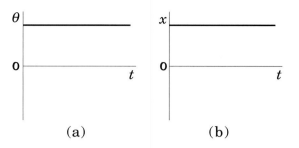

(a)   (b)

A3. (a) Which of the objects might have the angular velocity (ω) vs. time plot to the right? Explain.

(b) Which of the objects might have the velocity (v_x) vs. time plot to the right? Explain.

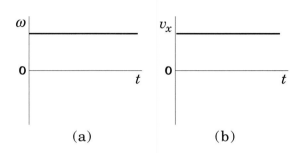

(a)   (b)

A4. (a) Which of the objects might have the angular velocity (ω) vs. time plot to the right? Explain.

(b) Which of the objects might have the velocity (v_x) vs. time plot to the right? Explain.

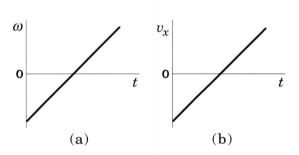

(a)   (b)

A5. (a) Which of the objects might have the angular acceleration (α) vs. time plot to the right? Explain.

(b) Which of the objects might have the acceleration (a_x) vs. time plot to the right? Explain.

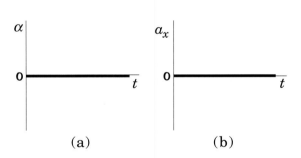

(a)   (b)

A6. (a) Which of the objects might have the angular acceleration (α) vs. time plot to the right? Explain.

(b) Which of the objects might have the acceleration (a_x) vs. time plot to the right? Explain.

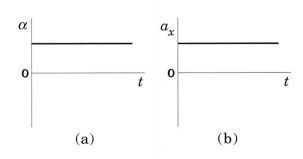

(a)   (b)

Reflection

R1. Reconsider situation B, in which a baseball is attached to a light rod that rotates at a constant rate due to a motor attached to the pivot. The arrangement completes one revolution every 5 seconds.

    (a) Make a strobe diagram showing the position of the ball every second for 10 seconds.

    (b) Plot the angular position θ vs. time t for 10 seconds.

    (c) Can the angular position be negative? Explain.

    (d) Can the angular position be larger than 360°? Explain.

    (e) Plot the angular velocity ω vs. time t for 10 seconds.

    (f) What is the slope of your angular position vs. time graph?

R2. (a) What motion quantity corresponds to the slope of angular position vs. time? Explain.

    (b) What motion quantity corresponds to the slope of angular velocity vs. time? Explain.

    (c) What motion quantity corresponds to the area below angular velocity vs. time? Explain.

R3. (a) For how many of the twelve graphs was there no object that matched the graph?

    (b) Which graphs did not correspond to any of the seven objects given?

    (c) For each of these graphs, create, draw, and describe a situation that matches the graph.

AT·17

Introducing Rotational Kinematics

Purpose and Expected Outcome

This is the second in a series of activities that studies rotational motion in analogy with linear motion. The structure of the activities is different from what you are used to. Within the next six activities, each pair of activities will focus on a particular subtopic of rotational motion, namely *kinematics*, *dynamics*, and *energy*.

In this activity, you will begin studying rotational kinematics. You will learn that you already have done some rotational kinematics, though not as formally as you will here. You will learn that rotational kinematics is *analogous* to linear kinematics, in that rotational and linear kinematics share many features, but they are still different. You will learn more about *angular* quantities, such as *angular acceleration*, *angular velocity*, and *angular position*.

Prior Experience / Knowledge Needed

You should know linear kinematics. You should know how to sketch graphs of position, velocity, and acceleration vs. time, and you should know the relationships among position, velocity, and acceleration. You should know how to write velocity and position as functions of time for constant acceleration. You should be able to use given information about the position and/or velocity of an object to predict its position and/or velocity at other times.

You should know that there are 360° or 2π radians in a circle. You should have some experience with angular quantities, such as angular velocity and angular acceleration.

Explanation of Activity

There are two parts in this activity.

PART A: Exploring Rotational Motion

Consider a standard wall clock, with an hour hand, a minute hand, and a second hand, as shown below. All questions in this part refer to this situation. You may assume that the clock is about 12in (30cm) wide.

A1. Through how many degrees does the second hand move every second? Explain.

A2. Through how many degrees does the minute hand move every second? Explain.

A3. (a) Through how many <u>radians</u> does the second hand move every second?

(b) What is the *angular speed* of the second hand in radians/second?

(c) How would you describe the <u>direction</u> of the movement of the second hand? Explain.

A4. A bug is crawling very slowly along the second hand.
(a) Where would the speed of the bug be the largest? Explain.
(b) How fast is the bug moving when it is moving its fastest? Explain.
(c) Does the bug experience an *angular acceleration*? Explain.
(d) Is it possible for the bug to remain at rest while clinging to the second hand? Explain.

A5. (a) Sketch a graph of the angle that the second hand makes with the vertical vs. time.
(b) At what time(s) is the second hand vertical? Explain.
(c) What is the slope of this graph at $t = 17$s?
(d) Sketch a graph of the *angular velocity* of the second hand vs. time.

A6. How does the angular speed of the hour hand compare to the angular speed of someone standing on the Earth (as it spins on its axis)? Explain.

A7. How does the angular speed of someone standing on the Earth (as it spins) compare to the angular speed of the Earth traveling around the Sun? Explain.

PART B: Comparing Linear and Rotational Kinematics

The following situations are paired to give you a sense of how similar angular and linear kinematics are to each other. One involves linear motion, and the other involves rotational motion. Analyze each situation using your own common sense ideas about distance, speed, and time. Do not get bogged down in numerical values.

B1. Car A is driving down a long, straight highway at 60mi/h (29m/s). Car B is driving around a circular track, also at 60mi/h. The radius of the track is 50m.

(a) Which car travels a longer distance in 40 minutes? Explain.

(b) Which car takes longer to go 80 miles? Explain.

(c) How long does it take for car B to complete one revolution of the track?

(d) How many revolutions does car B make in 10 minutes?

(e) What is the *angular velocity* of car B in revolutions per second? (**Hints:** How many revolutions does the car make in one second? What is the direction of the car's motion?)

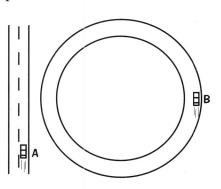

B2. Car A is driving down a long, straight highway at 45mi/h (20m/s). Car B is driving around a circular track, also at 45mi/h. (See diagram for B1 above.) The radius of the track is 50m. Both cars accelerate for six seconds until they are going 60mi/h (29m/s).

(a) Which car has the larger acceleration? Explain.

(b) What is the change in velocity of car A? What is the acceleration of car A?

(c) What is the change in angular velocity of car B in rev/s? What is the *angular acceleration* of car B in rev/s²? (**Hints:** What is the change in angular velocity every second? What is the direction of this change?)

B3. At the instant shown, a wheel is spinning at 2rev/s, and slowing down at a constant rate of $1/2$rev/s². A white line helps keep track of its position. A ball is rolling up an incline at 8m/s, and slowing down at a rate of 2m/s².

(a) Which object stops first? Explain.

(b) Write an expression for the position of the ball as a function of time. (Let $x_0 = 0.8$m.)

(c) Write an expression for the *angular position* of the wheel as a function of time. (Let $\theta_0 = 0.2$rev, and assume that the initial angular velocity is <u>negative</u>.)

(d) Specify the position of each object at $t = 6$s.

(e) Rewrite your expression in (c) using radians.

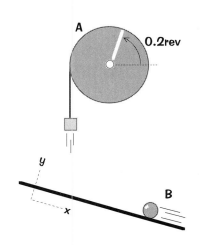

Summary

By convention, we measure the angle θ in the counterclockwise direction relative the horizontal. So, in the diagram, $\theta = 72°$. Counterclockwise (CCW) rotations mean that the angle θ is getting more positive, so CCW motion corresponds to a positive angular velocity. In the diagram, the motion is clockwise (CW) so the angular velocity is negative, because the angle θ is getting more negative.

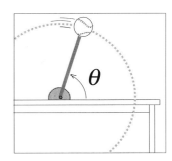

Reflection

R1. (a) What is the <u>ratio</u> of the angular speeds of the second hand and the minute hand on a clock? Explain your method for determining this ratio. Compare your method with that of your classmates.

(b) Which is easier to determine: the ratio of the angular speeds or the individual angular speeds of the two hands? Explain.

R2. (a) Estimate the angular velocity of someone in Puerto Rico due to the spinning Earth. Is your answer positive or negative? Why?

(b) Estimate the angular velocity of someone near the South Pole. Is your answer positive or negative? Why?

(c) Estimate the angular velocity of the second hand on a clock. Is your answer positive or negative? Why?

(d) Estimate your angular acceleration (due to a spinning Earth). Explain.

R3. Which are harder to answer: questions about linear motion or questions about rotational motion? Why?

R4. (a) Is it possible for an object to have a non-zero acceleration and zero angular acceleration? If not, explain why not. If so, give an example.

(b) Is it possible for an object to have zero acceleration and a non-zero angular acceleration? If not, explain why not. If so, give an example.

R5. If something has a negative angular acceleration, is it speeding up or slowing down? Why? Give an example of a situation in which the angular acceleration is negative, but the object is speeding up. Also, give an example of a situation in which the angular acceleration is positive, but the object is slowing down.

Solving Rotational Kinematics Problems

Purpose and Expected Outcome

This is the third in a series of activities that studies rotational motion in analogy with linear motion. The structure of the activities is different from what you are used to. Each pair of activities in the series will focus on a particular subtopic of rotational motion, such as *kinematics*, *dynamics*, and *energy*.

This is the second activity focusing on rotational kinematics. You will be learn how to analyze rotational systems using *angular* quantities, such as *angular acceleration*, *angular velocity*, and *angular position*. You will be able to solve rotational motion problems by thinking about how an analogous linear motion problem would be solved.

Prior Experience / Knowledge Needed

You should know linear kinematics. You should know how to sketch graphs of position, velocity, and acceleration vs. time, and you should know the relationships among position, velocity, and acceleration. You should know how to write velocity and position as functions of time for constant acceleration. You should be able to use given information about the position and/or velocity of an object to predict its position and/or velocity at other times.

You should know that there are 360° or 2π radians in a circle. You should be familiar with rotational motion quantities, and you should be able to sketch angular position, angular velocity, and angular acceleration vs. time.

Explanation of Activity

Solve each of the problems described below. If necessary, translate the problem to an analogous linear motion problem, and think about how you would solve it.

A1. A baseball is attached to a rigid rod. At the instant shown, the arrangement has an angular speed of 4π radians per second (4π rad/s). Its angular acceleration is constant throughout the motion. The arrangement slows down, coming to a stop 5 seconds later, and reverses direction.

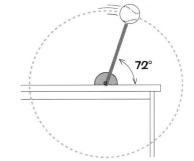

    (a) What is the initial angular velocity of the arrangement?

    (b) Sketch a graph of angular velocity vs. time from $t = 0$s until $t = 10$s.

    (c) Sketch a graph of angular position vs. time from $t = 0$s until $t = 10$s.

    (d) What is the angular acceleration of the arrangement?

    (e) What is the change in angular position for the arrangement during the entire 10s time interval?

    (f) When has the arrangement rotated farthest from its initial angular position? Through what angle has it rotated?

A2. Andri is riding her mountain bike. At $t = 0$s, she starts to slow down. The angular velocity ω of the front wheel is shown to the right.

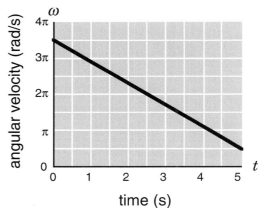

    (a) How fast is the wheel spinning initially?

    (b) Estimate how fast Andri is moving initially.

    (c) What is the angular acceleration of the wheel?

    (d) Estimate Andri's acceleration.

    (e) What is the *angular displacement* of the wheel during the 5s time period shown? (Express your answer in both radians and degrees.)

    (f) Estimate how far Andri travels during the 5s time interval shown.

    (g) When does Andri stop?

continued

A3. Two disks are mounted on a frictionless axle as shown. The upper disk is at rest initially, and the bottom disk spins frictionlessly at an angular speed of $\omega_0 = 20$rad/s. At $t = 0$s, the stationary disk is lowered onto the moving disk. Friction between the two disks causes each to accelerate. Because the upper disk is smaller, its rate of acceleration is four times as large as the rate for the lower disk.

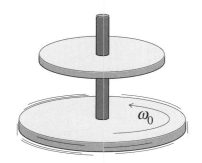

(a) On a single set of axes, sketch the angular velocities for the two disks as functions of time.

(b) When do you suppose they will stop accelerating? Describe the conditions that indicate when—and why!—the two disks stop accelerating.

(c) Determine the final angular velocities of the two disks.

A4. The hard disk on your computer is "spinning up" according to the graph at right when a malfunction occurs, and the hard disk slows down again.

(a) When does the malfunction occur?

(b) What is the angular displacement of the hard disk up until the malfunction?

(c) What is the angular displacement of the hard disk during the 5s time interval shown?

(d) What is the *average* angular acceleration of the disk during the 5s time interval shown?

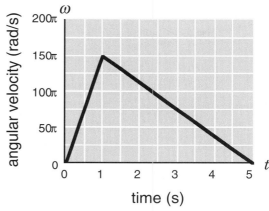

A5. Within any particular gear, the angular speed of a car's engine is roughly proportional to the speed of the car. For a certain car, when the engine spins at 2000rpm (revolutions per minute), the car's speed is 45mi/h (20m/s).

(a) How fast is the car going when the engine spins at 3000rpm?

(b) If the car speeds up to 60mi/h (29m/s) in 3 seconds, what is the average angular acceleration of the car's engine?

Reflection

R1. What do you find most difficult about solving problems in rotational kinematics?

R2. For any of the situations or questions, did you think about what an analogous linear motion problem might look like? Why or why not?

R3. Reconsider problem A1, in which a ball is attached to a rigid rod.

(a) Create a problem that is identical to it in structure, but involves only linear motion (that is, no rotational motion).

(b) Which problem is easier to solve? Why?

R4. Reconsider situation A2, in which Andri is riding her mountain bike.

(a) What information did you need to estimate in order to answer part (b)?

(b) What is the relationship between displacement and angular displacement for a wheel rolling along the ground? Draw a picture to help you describe this relationship.

(c) What is the relationship between speed and angular speed for a wheel rolling along the ground? Explain why this is true.

(d) What is the relationship between acceleration and angular acceleration for a wheel rolling along the ground? Explain your reasoning.

R5. Reconsider situation A3, in which two disks are mounted on a common axle.

(a) When the two disks are first in contact with each other, what type of friction does each exert on the other? Explain.

(b) What happens later when the disks are rotating at the same rate? Does the force of friction stay the same or change? What happens to the angular accelerations of the two disks?

(c) Could you use this information to help you solve the problem? How?

(d) If you could not solve the problem, go back and try again, this time keeping in mind the type of friction exerted by the two disks on each other.

R6. Reconsider situation A5, involving a car and its engine.

(a) Describe a situation in which the angular speed of the car's engine is certainly <u>not</u> proportional to its speed.

(b) In order to answer the questions (A5(a) and A5(b)), what did you assume about the gear that the car was in? Were you aware that you had assumed this? Explain.

Introducing Rotational Dynamics

Purpose and Expected Outcome

This is the fourth in a series of activities covering rotational motion. In this activity, you will start learning about rotational *dynamics*, which involves the forces exerted on rotating systems and the response of those systems (i.e., angular acceleration). You will learn why we need to introduce two new quantities: *torque* and *moment of inertia*.

Prior Experience / Knowledge Needed

You should know dynamics. You should know Newton's laws and how to apply them to physical situations. You should have some experience analyzing and solving problems in dynamics. You should know how to apply empirical laws for forces.

You should have some experience with angular quantities, such as angular position, angular velocity, and angular acceleration.

Explanation of Activity

The following situations will give you a sense of why we need to treat rotational systems differently than linear systems, and why we need to introduce new quantities. Many situations can be done hands-on, so first predict what you think will happen, then try it yourself.

A1. A door is hinged as shown. Two people push from either side of the door, keeping it at rest.

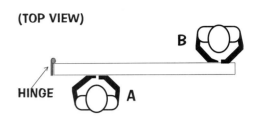

(TOP VIEW)

(a) Which person is pushing harder on the door? Explain.

(b) How much harder do you suppose that person is pushing? Explain.

A2. Imagine two different arrangements of the same materials. Coins are attached <u>securely</u> to a cardboard disk, and a pencil is poked through its center. The same number of coins is used for each, but in A, the coins are spread evenly over the cardboard, and in B, the coins are stacked near the outer edge.

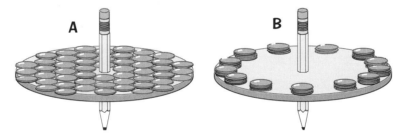

(a) If you apply the same "twisting" forces to the both pencils, which arrangement will accelerate faster? Explain.

(b) How much faster do you suppose that one accelerates? (By what factor?)

A3. A pencil is stuck into an eraser as shown, and balanced on a cardboard triangle.

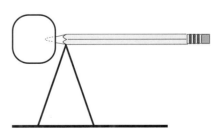

(a) Which is heavier, the pencil or the eraser? Explain.

(b) Why do they balance, even though the weights on either side are different?

continued

A4. Consider a meter stick. Is it easier to get the meter stick spinning around its center (A) or around its end (B)? Explain.

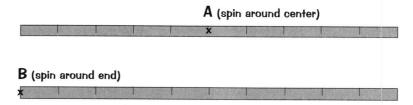

A5. Mountain bikes and ten-speeds have two or three gears in the front (on the same axle as the pedals), and five or six gears in the back (on the same axle as the rear wheel).

(a) For which of the front gears is it easiest to pedal? Explain.

(b) For which of the back gears is it easiest to pedal? Explain.

(c) If you were to pedal at the same rate with all combinations, which would result in the smallest speed of the bike? Which would result in the largest speed?

(d) Estimate the ratio of the largest speed and the smallest speed of the bike.

Summary

Two new quantities are needed to understand rotational motion, *torque* and *moment of inertia*. *Torque* is a force-like quantity that depends on four factors: (1) the strength of the force applied; (2) the direction of the force applied; (3) the location at which the force is applied; and (4) the location of the fixed axis "about which" the torque is desired. For example, in A1, the door remains at rest even though the two people exert different forces. Both people exert the same torque (relative to the hinge) in opposite directions, so the net result is that the torques are balanced.

Similarly, in situation A3, the eraser and pencil are balanced on the cardboard triangle, not because the weights are the same, but because the torques are balanced.

Moment of inertia is a mass-like quantity that depends on three factors: (1) the mass of the object; (2) the distribution of mass; and (3) the location of the fixed axis "about which" the moment of inertia is desired. The moment of inertia tells you how easy or hard it will be to get an object spinning about a certain axis (just as the mass tells you how easy or hard it will be to accelerate something). For instance, in A2, both disks have the same mass, but one is harder to get spinning, because the mass is farther from the axis. Disk B has the larger moment of inertia relative to the axis of rotation.

Situation A4 is different. The masses of both meter sticks are the same, and the mass is distributed the same also, but A is easier to get spinning than B because the moment of inertia about the center is smaller than the moment of inertia about the end.

Reflection

R1. In situation A1, relative to the <u>right</u> side of the door (the unhinged side)...

    (a) ... which person exerts the larger torque, or are they the same? Explain.

    (b) ... are the torques on the door balanced or unbalanced? Explain why you think so.

R2. For how many situations did you predict something that did not happen? Why do you suppose these predictions were incorrect? What did you learn as a result?

R3. Create an arrangement for which the moment of inertia about one end is different from the moment of inertia about the other end. Can you predict which moment of inertia will be larger? How?

R4. Consider an open door, hinged at one end as shown. Two people, A and B, are exerting forces as shown.

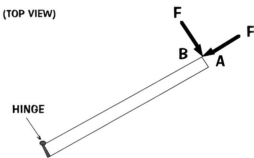

    (a) Which person do you suppose is more responsible for closing the door? Explain.

    (b) Of the four factors given for the torque in the Summary, which are different for the two torques exerted by the two people? Explain.

    (c) If these two forces are exerted at different times, which will produce the larger angular acceleration of the door? Explain.

R5. Reconsider situation A4, in which two people attempt to spin a meter stick about different points. Person C is given two meter sticks held together by rubber bands as shown.

    (a) Person C attempts to get this arrangement spinning through its center. Is it harder or easier to get it spinning than for person A?

    (b) Which factor for the moment of inertia is different for person C than person A? Explain.

Solving Rotational Dynamics Problems

Purpose and Expected Outcome

In this activity, you will learn more about rotational *dynamics*, which involves the forces exerted on rotating systems and the response of those systems (i.e., angular acceleration). You will learn how to apply the concepts of *torque* and *moment of inertia* to problem situations involving rotating systems.

Prior Experience / Knowledge Needed

You should know dynamics. You should know Newton's laws and how to apply them to physical situations. You should have some experience analyzing and solving problems in dynamics, and you should know how to apply empirical force laws. In addition, you should have some experience with rotational kinematics, and you should be able to recognize when a system is accelerating. You should know the definitions of *torque, net torque,* and *moment of inertia* relative to a fixed axis.

NEWTON'S 2ND LAW IN ROTATIONAL FORM

Newton's 2nd law ($\mathbf{F}_{net} = m\,\mathbf{a}$) is valid and applicable for all objects and systems. However, when a rigid body is spinning about a fixed axis, it is more convenient to use angular quantities, such as angular velocity and angular acceleration, to describe its motion. (At any particular instant, every part of the rigid body has a different velocity but the same angular velocity.) In terms of angular acceleration, Newton's 2nd law is written:

$$\tau_{net,p} = I_p \alpha_p \qquad \text{Newton's 2nd law for rotations about a fixed axis}$$

where $\tau_{net,p}$ is the net torque on the rigid body about a fixed axis through point p, I_p is the object's the moment of inertia for rotations about the same axis, and α_p is its angular acceleration. Note that $\tau_{net,p}$ and α_p are vectors.

Explanation of Activity

Solve each of the problems described below. If necessary, translate the problem to a linear dynamics problem, and think about how you would solve it.

A1. A 10g hanger is placed on a device as shown. The pegs are evenly spaced and labeled 1 through 13. Hangers of various masses are available.

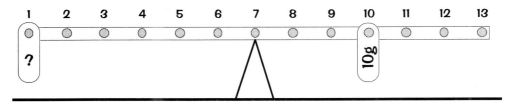

(a) What mass will balance the 10g hanger when placed on peg #1? Explain why it balances.

(b) Where should you put a 15g hanger to balance the 10g hanger? (The unknown hanger is removed.)

(c) Where should you put a 3g and a 4g hanger (at the same time) to balance the 10g hanger?

(d) Is it possible to balance the arrangement with <u>only</u> the 10g hanger (and nothing else)? If so, how? If not, explain why not.

(e) How many ways are there to arrange a 2g, a 3g, and a 5g hanger so that each is on its own peg, and the arrangement is balanced? Describe at least two arrangements. (The 10g hanger is removed.)

A2. A string is wound around a metal wheel that is free to spin on a frictionless pivot. A hanging mass is connected to the other end of the string. The wheel is given a twist, causing it to start rotating at $2^{1}/_{2}$ rad/s in the counterclockwise direction. All known quantities are shown in the figure.

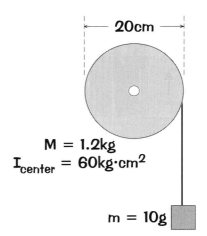

(a) What is the initial velocity of the hanging mass?

(b) Estimate the angular acceleration of the disk.

(c) Approximately when does the disk stop? Explain.

(d) Estimate the velocity of the mass at $t = 2$s.

(e) Estimate the acceleration of the mass at $t = 3$s.

continued

A3. A bicycle is supported off the ground using a clamp (shown in the scale drawing) attached to the post. The wheel weighs about 50N, and a force of 15N is applied to the pedal.

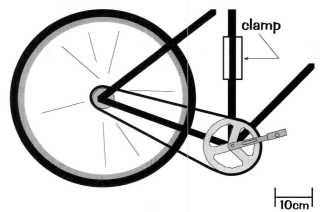

(a) Estimate the moment of inertia of the wheel.

(b) Estimate the net torque applied to the front gear, the tension in the chain, and the net torque applied to the back gear.

(c) Estimate the angular acceleration of the wheel.

10cm

A4. Two masses are attached to strings wound around a double pulley as shown. The double pulley has a total mass of 1200g (1.2kg), and the total moment of inertia about its center is 50,000g·cm² (0.005kg·m²).

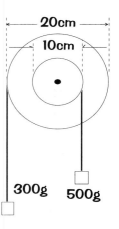

(a) If the arrangement is released from rest, which direction will it start to rotate? Explain.

(b) Estimate the angular acceleration of the double pulley.

(c) Which mass is traveling faster at any instant, or are they traveling with the same speed? Explain. If their speeds are different, what is the ratio of their speeds?

(d) Estimate the velocity of the 300g mass at $t = 2$s.

A5. The hard disk on your computer is "spinning up" according to the graph at right when a malfunction occurs, and the hard disk slows down again.

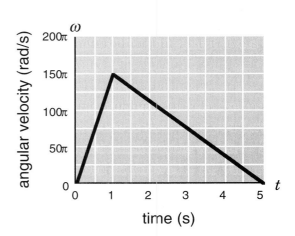

(a) If the net torque exerted on the hard disk initially is about 0.08N·m, estimate the hard disk's moment of inertia.

(b) What is the net torque exerted on the hard disk after the malfunction?

(c) What is the net torque exerted on the hard disk at $t = 5$s? Explain.

Reflection

R1. What do you find most difficult about solving problems in rotational dynamics?

R2. For any of the situations or problems, did you think about what the linear motion situation or problem might look like? Why or why not?

R3. (a) What is the general relationship between the angular displacement $\Delta\theta$ of a spinning wheel and the displacement Δy of a mass hanging from a string wound around the wheel? Explain. In your relationship, what are the units of the angular displacement? Why?

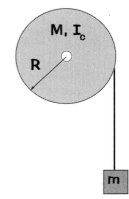

(b) What is the general relationship between the angular velocity ω of the wheel and the velocity v_y of the hanging mass? Explain.

(c) What is the general relationship between the angular acceleration α of the wheel and the acceleration a_y of the hanging mass? Explain.

R4. Reconsider situation A2, in which a hanging mass is attached to a string wound around a solid wheel.

(a) When the arrangement is free to spin, which is larger, the tension in the string or the weight of the hanging mass? Explain your reasoning.

(b) Did you ignore this difference when you solved problem A2? Did you <u>know</u> that you had ignored this difference?

(c) How does this affect your answers? (If you do not ignore this difference, which answers become slightly larger, which ones stay the same, and which ones become slightly smaller?)

R5. Reconsider situation A3, in which a bicycle is held off the ground with a clamp.

(a) What features did you ignore to answer the questions?

(b) How would your answers change if you did not ignore these features? (If you did not ignore these features, which answers would be larger, which would stay the same, and which would be smaller?)

R6. Is it possible to exert a force at the <u>edge</u> of an object without exerting a torque about its center? Give an example of a situation involving a bicycle wheel in which a force is exerted to the <u>rim</u> of the wheel, but no torque is exerted about the center of the wheel.

AT·21

Identifying Energy in Rotational Systems

Purpose and Expected Outcome

This is the sixth in a series of activities about rotational motion. We have covered rotational kinematics and dynamics. In this activity, you will learn about the energy in rotating systems, and its similarities and differences with forms of energy you have learned about already.

Prior Experience / Knowledge Needed

You should know linear kinematics, linear dynamics, and Conservation of Energy applied to non-rotating systems. You should know the definition of work, kinetic energy, and potential energy.

You should be familiar with rotational kinematics and rotational dynamics. You should be familiar with rotational quantities, such as angular position, angular velocity, angular acceleration, torque, and moment of inertia.

Explanation of Activity

There are two parts in this activity.

PART A: Comparing the Kinetic Energy in Different Situations

Consider the five arrangements of mass shown below. All five have the same total mass M. Arrangements A and E have the same radius R, but in A, the mass is concentrated at the rim, while in E, the mass is uniformly distributed. Arrangement B is also a wheel, but its radius is half that of A and E. Arrangement C is a mass M attached a distance R from the pivot, and arrangement D has two masses (each $1/2\,M$) spinning as shown. All five arrangements are spinning with the same angular velocity ω.

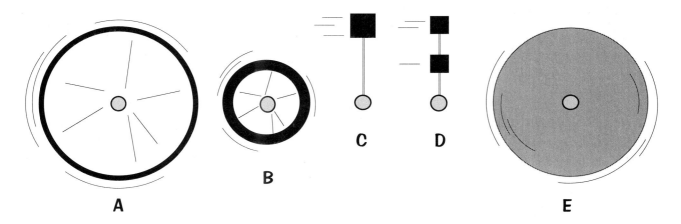

Use what you <u>already know</u> about kinetic energy to reason out your responses.

A1. Which arrangement has the larger kinetic energy, A or B? Explain.

A2. Which has the larger kinetic energy, A or C? Explain.

A3. Which has the larger kinetic energy, A or D? Explain.

A4. Which has the larger kinetic energy, A or E? Explain.

A5. Which arrangement has the largest kinetic energy? Explain.

A6. Which arrangement has the smallest kinetic energy? Explain.

A7. Put the five arrangements in order of their kinetic energies, from smallest to largest. Explain your reasoning.

PART B: Analyzing More Situations

Answer the following questions about the energy in various situations.

B1. Imagine two different arrangements of the same materials. Coins are <u>securely</u> attached to a cardboard disk, and a pencil is poked through its center. The same number of coins is used for each, but in A, the coins are spread evenly over the cardboard, and in B, the coins are stacked near the outer edge. Which disk has more energy when it has an angular speed of 2π rad/s? Explain.

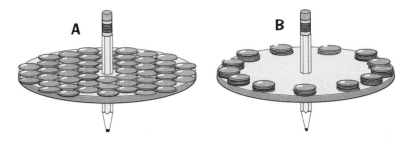

B2. Two identical wheels are spinning, but wheel A is spinning twice as fast as the other (B).

(a) Which wheel has more kinetic energy? Explain.

(b) By what factor does this wheel have more kinetic energy? Explain.

B3. Nickels (5 grams each) are securely attached to a light piece of cardboard as shown in the scale drawing below. The arrangement spins around its center at 2 revolutions per second.

(a) What is the total mass of the arrangement?

(b) Estimate the kinetic energy of one of the outermost nickels. Explain your estimate.

(c) Estimate the kinetic energy of one of the innermost nickels. Explain your estimate.

(d) Estimate the total kinetic energy of the arrangement.

(e) If the arrangement were spinning only half as fast, by what factor would the kinetic energy change? Explain.

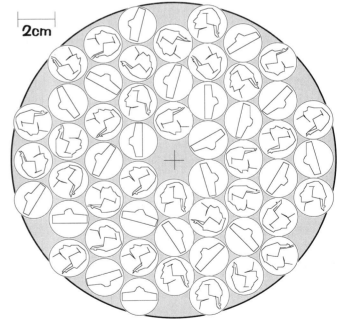

2cm

Reflection

R1. Reconsider the situations used for part A, in which 5 different arrangements of mass are spinning at the same rate ω.

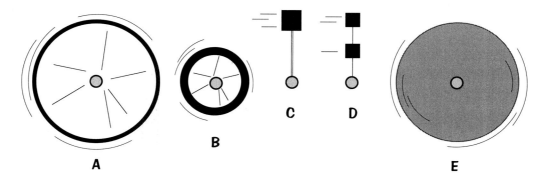

(a) Of A and E, which arrangement has the larger mass? Explain.

(b) Of A and E, which has the larger moment of inertia? Explain.

(c) Of A and E, which requires the larger torque about its center to keep it spinning? Explain.

(d) Of A and E, which has the larger kinetic energy? Explain.

R2. The front wheel of a standard mountain bike is about 26 inches (about 66cm) in diameter and has a weight of about $3^{1}/_{2}$lb (mass about 1600g).

(a) Estimate the wheel's moment of inertia about its center.

(b) How much energy is needed to get the wheel spinning at 2rev/s?

R3. What features of a rigid object determine its total kinetic energy?

R4. Reconsider situation B3, in which nickels are attached to a piece of cardboard and the arrangement is spun through its center at 2 revolutions per second.

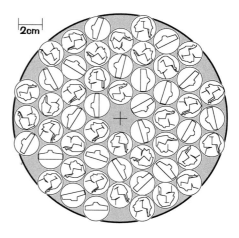

(a) How many nickels are there in the arrangement?

Imagine making a list consisting of the kinetic energy of each individual nickel.

(b) How many unique values for the kinetic energy would there be in your list? Explain how you determined this number.

(b) How many nickels have the smallest kinetic energy? Which ones?

(c) How many nickels have the largest kinetic energy? Which ones?

Solving Problems with Energy in Rotational Systems

Purpose and Expected Outcome

In this activity, you will learn how to apply energy ideas to problems involving systems containing rotating parts.

Prior Experience / Knowledge Needed

You should know linear kinematics, linear dynamics, and Conservation of Energy for linear systems. You should know the definition of work, kinetic energy, and potential energy.

You should be familiar with rotational kinematics and rotational dynamics. You should be familiar with quantities needed for rotational motion, such as angular position, angular velocity, angular acceleration, torque, net torque, and moment of inertia. You should have some experience with identifying energy in rotating systems.

ENERGY IN ROTATING SYSTEMS

When a rigid object is spinning about a fixed axis, it has a total kinetic energy equal to the sum of the kinetic energies of every part of the object. Applying the definition of kinetic energy for a point object ($E_K \equiv 1/2 mv^2$) and adding up the contributions for the entire rigid object, we get:

$$E_K = 1/2 I_p \omega_p^2 \qquad \text{kinetic energy for rotations about a fixed axis}$$

where I_p is the moment of inertia for rotation about a fixed axis through point p, and ω_p is the angular speed about point p.

Explanation of Activity

There are two parts in this activity.

PART A: Solving Rotational Motion Problems Using Energy Ideas

Solve each of the problems described below. If necessary, translate the problem to a linear problem, and think about how you would solve it.

A1. A 240g ball is attached to a light 30cm rod and held horizontally as shown. The ball is released from rest.

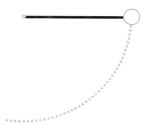

  (a) Find the maximum (linear) speed of the ball using ideas you learned previously about energy. (In other words, use NO rotational quantities to find the speed of the ball.)

  (b) What is the arrangement's moment of inertia about the pivot?

  (c) Find the maximum angular speed of the arrangement using rotational ideas and quantities.

A2. A mass m is attached to a long string, which is wound around a disk having radius R, mass M, and moment of inertia about its center I_c. The system is released from rest.

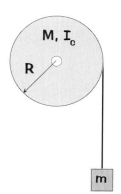

  (a) Find the speed of the mass after falling a distance h. (Your answer must be left in terms of given or known quantities.)

  (b) What is the angular speed of the disk after it has rotated through one complete revolution?

  (c) For m = 200g, R = 40cm, M = 2kg, and I_c = 0.16kg·m², find numerical values for your answers to (a) and (b).

A3. The hard disk on your computer is spinning up according to the graph at right when a malfunction occurs, and the hard disk slows down again. The disk's moment of inertia is about 1600g·cm².

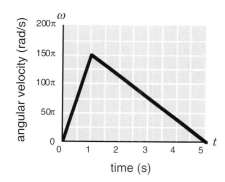

  (a) Estimate the total amount of work done on the hard disk from t = 0s to t = ¹/₂s.

  (b) Estimate the amount of macroscopic energy converted to microscopic energy. Explain.

A4. An amusement park ride is made to swing its passengers in a large circular arc. A motor attached to the pivot is used primarily to overcome frictional losses of energy, and none of the passengers may ever be above the pivot. The swinging part of the ride weighs about 6000kg and seats at most 60 passengers. Estimate the maximum speed of the passengers.

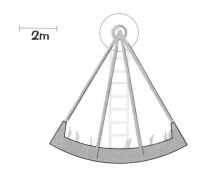

PART B: Solving More Complex Problems Using Energy Ideas

These problems are more difficult than what you are used to. If you get stuck, try to break down the problem into more manageable pieces, then put them together again to solve the problem.

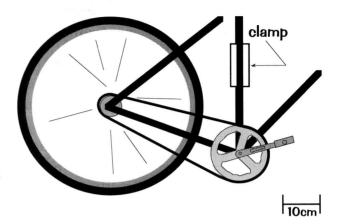

B1. A bicycle is supported off the ground using a clamp (shown) attached to the post. The wheel weighs about 50N, and a force of 15N is applied to the pedal.

    (a) Estimate the moment of inertia of the wheel.

    (b) How much work is needed to get the <u>pedal</u> moving at 2rev/s? Explain.

B2. In developed areas likely to be left without power for long periods of time (due to severe lightning storms, for example), residents might use a *flywheel* to store energy. Typically the flywheel is made from a dense material, such as concrete, in the shape of a thick solid disk that fits easily in the back of a garage or basement. Nearly frictionless bearings permit the wheel to spin with almost no energy losses. When needed, the spinning flywheel is engaged to provide the power needed to run a one-family home. The moment of inertia of a solid disk is $1/2 MR^2$.

    (a) Estimate the dimensions of the flywheel. How much does the flywheel weigh?

    (b) Estimate how fast the flywheel must spin to provide power for a one-family home for one week. Explain your estimate. Indicate the values of all quantities needed to complete your estimate, and indicate how you determined each value.

B3. A *torsional spring* is made from a rigid metal rod attached firmly to the ceiling. A 2kg solid disk having a diameter of 20cm and a thickness of $1^1/2$cm is attached to the other end of the metal rod. A torque about the center of the disk of $1/2$N·m causes the disk to rotate 30°. The disk is rotated 180° and released from rest.

    (a) What torque about the center of the disk is needed to rotate the disk through 180°? Explain.

    (b) How much energy is stored in the metal rod initially? Explain.

    (c) What is the maximum angular speed of the disk? Explain.

Reflection

R1. What do you find most difficult about solving problems involving energy in rotating systems?

R2. For any of the situations or problems, did you think about what the situation or problem might look like without anything rotating or spinning? Why or why not?

R3. Which has the larger moment of inertia...
  (a) ... a solid disk of mass M and radius R or a ring of mass M and radius R? Explain.
  (b) ... a solid disk of mass M, radius R and thickness h, or a solid disk of mass M, radius R and thickness $2h$? Explain.
  (c) ... a solid disk spinning with angular speed ω or an identical disk spinning with angular speed 2ω? Explain.
  (d) ... a solid disk of density ρ, radius R and thickness h or a ring of density ρ, radius R and thickness h? Explain.

R4. What are the proper units of angular displacement, angular speed, and angular acceleration? What do you find most difficult about using these units?

R5. Reconsider problem A1, in which a ball is attached to a light rod and allowed to swing freely. Convert your maximum angular speed found in part (c) to a maximum speed for the ball. Does your answer agree with your answer in part (a) for the maximum speed of the ball? Explain any differences.

R6. Consider the following problem:

A 2kg cart rolls frictionlessly along a horizontal surface at 1.3m/s. A horizontal force is exerted on the cart to stop it.
  (a) How much work is done on the cart to stop it?
  (b) If it takes 4 seconds to stop the cart, what force is exerted on the cart?
  (c) How far does the cart roll before stopping?

Create a problem involving rotational ideas and motion that shares the same *deep structure* as this problem. (This means that your problem would be solved by applying similar or analogous principles, even though the situation is completely different.)

AT·23

Solving Problems in Rotational Motion

Purpose and Expected Outcome

In this activity you will solve problems involving rotating systems. You will learn how to distinguish among problems involving rotational kinematics, rotational dynamics, and energy of rotating systems.

Prior Experience / Knowledge Needed

You should be familiar with rotational motion, including kinematics, dynamics and energy. You also need to know the main principles of mechanics and how to use them to solve problems.

Explanation of Activity

Below are four problems involving rotational motion but also involving other useful principles and ideas. Be prepared to discuss your answers with your classmates.

A1. A baseball is attached to a rigid rod as shown at $t = 0$s to the right. The graph below shows the angular velocity of the system as a function of time.

(a) In which direction (i.e., clockwise or counterclockwise) is the system rotating initially?

(b) What happens at $t = 10$s?

(c) How much work is done on the system between $t = 0$s and $t = 10$s?

(d) How much work is done on the system between $t = 0$s and $t = 50$s?

(e) When is the angular acceleration of the system the largest? Explain. When is it the smallest? Explain.

(f) How many revolutions does the system make during the 50s time period shown?

(g) Estimate the torque exerted on the system at $t = 10$s, 30s, and 40s.

(h) Draw a picture showing what the system looks like at $t = 50$s.

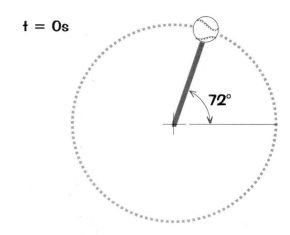

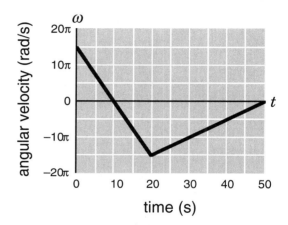

A2. Two masses are attached to strings wound around a double pulley. The double pulley has a total mass of about 600g (0.6kg), and the total moment of inertia about its center is 25,000g·cm^2 (0.0025kg·m^2). The system is released from rest as shown.

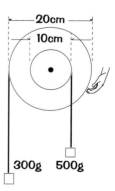

(a) In which direction (i.e., clockwise or counterclockwise) will the pulley rotate just after being released?

(b) When the 500g hanging mass has moved 15cm, what are the velocities of the two masses?

continued

A3. A *torsional spring* is made from a rigid metal rod attached firmly to the ceiling. A 6kg disk, with a radius of 10cm and a moment of inertia of 0.03kg·m², is attached to the other end of the rod. The torques required to twist the rod through various angular displacements are shown in the graph to the far right.

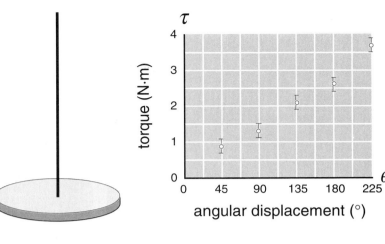

(a) Estimate the *torsional spring constant K*.

(b) Where—and how—should a force be applied to the disk to minimize the force needed to keep the system twisted and at rest?

(c) What is the smallest force that will keep the disk at rest rotated through 45°?

Assume now that the disk is given an initial angular speed of 5rad/s when the angular displacement is zero.

(d) What is the largest angular position the disk can reach?

(e) What happens to the disk after it returns to its equilibrium position for the first time? (For instance, does it stop or does it keep going? Where does it stop again?)

(f) Sketch the angular velocity of the disk as a function of time.

A4. Consider the two arrangements shown to the right. In arrangement A, a long string is wound around a solid disk that is lying flat on a smooth table. In arrangement B, a short piece of string is tied securely to an identical disk. A constant tension of 18N is maintained in each string.

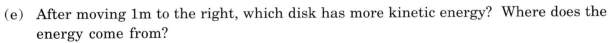

TOP VIEW

(a) What is the net force on each disk?

(b) Which disk has the larger (linear) acceleration?

(c) After 1 second, which disk has the larger speed?

(d) After 1 second, which disk has moved farther?

(e) After moving 1m to the right, which disk has more kinetic energy? Where does the energy come from?

(f) While moving 1m to the right, which disk has more work done on it?

Reflection

R1. (a) List the major concepts and principles within rotational motion that you needed to answer the questions in this activity.

(b) List the major concepts and principles within linear motion that you needed to answer the questions in this activity.

R2. (a) What concepts and/or principles within rotational motion do you need to learn better?

(b) What concepts and/or principles within linear motion do you need to learn better?

R3. In what ways has learning about rotational motion improved your understanding of linear motion? Give some examples.

R4. (a) What sketches or drawings did you use to help you solve these problems? Explain how they helped you.

(b) What sketches or drawings did your classmates use that you did not use? What are some reasons why you did not use them? Do you need to learn better how to use some of them?

R5. Reconsider situation A4, in which two disks are pulled by strings attached in different ways.

(a) Does Newton's 2nd law ($\mathbf{F}_{net} = m\mathbf{a}$) remain valid even though the object is spinning? Comment.

(b) Focus your attention on the end of the string that is pulled, and assume that the disks are side-by-side initially. Do the ends of the strings stay side-by-side as they are pulled, or does one go ahead of the other? If so, which one? Why? Which agent pulling the string does more work?

Reader

**ADVANCED
TOPICS IN
MECHANICS**

CIRCULAR, PROJECTILE & RELATIVE MOTION

This chapter consists of three sections, dealing with three largely independent topics. These three topics are similar, however, in that all are opportunities to apply the laws of physics to new situations.

In *circular motion*, you will learn how to relate kinematic information, such as speed and radius of curvature, to dynamic information, such as the forces exerted on objects moving in circles. In *projectile motion*, you will learn how to apply kinematic results derived in one dimension to two-dimensional motion. You will also learn how to analyze the forces on a projectile and how the energy of a projectile changes during a trajectory. In *relative motion*, you will learn how to describe the motion of an object from different perspectives. You will also learn some new features of energy conservation that you might not have realized before.

As you are working through these three subjects, remember that Newton's laws and the laws of conservation of momentum and energy remain true, even though they will seem to be more hidden than they were before.

1.1 CIRCULAR MOTION

The term *circular motion* refers to those situations in which an object moves along any finite, circular arc. The simplest of these situations is when something moves in a circle at constant speed, such as when a rock is swung in a horizontal circle or when a car goes around a curve in the road without slowing down. In slightly more difficult situations, the object moves in a circle, but the speed is not necessarily constant, such as when a pendulum swings. The most challenging situations are those in which both the radius of the circle and the speed of the object is changing, such as when someone rides a roller coaster. We will find that the ideas and relationships derived for motion along a circle can be successfully applied for motion along any curved path. These examples and others are shown at the top of the next page.

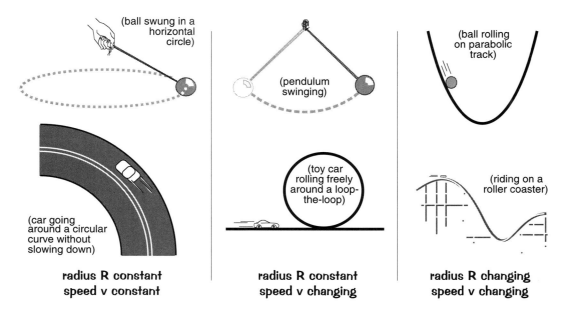

(car going around a circular curve without slowing down)	(toy car rolling freely around a loop-the-loop)	(riding on a roller coaster)
radius R constant speed v constant	radius R constant speed v changing	radius R changing speed v changing

situations that can be analyzed using circular motion ideas

1.1.1 Uniform circular motion. The simplest situations are those in which both the radius of curvature and the speed are constant. This is called *uniform* circular motion. Even though the speed is constant, because the direction of velocity is changing, the object is accelerating. There are two factors affecting how large the acceleration is. The larger the speed, the faster the direction changes, so the larger the acceleration. Also, the <u>smaller</u> the circle, the faster the direction changes, and the larger the acceleration. Therefore, the acceleration depends on the speed and the radius of curvature. We will now derive the exact relationship.

Consider a ball attached to a very light rod, which rotates at constant speed using a motor attached to the pivot. The radius of the circular path is R, and the speed of the ball is v. Note that the velocity is always directed along a tangent to the circle. Because the direction of motion is changing, the ball is accelerating.

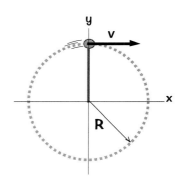

To find the relationship, we start with the definition of **a**:

$$\mathbf{a} \equiv \frac{\Delta \mathbf{v}}{\Delta t} \ (\Delta t \text{ very small}) \qquad \textbf{definition of acceleration}$$

In order to find the instantaneous acceleration, we will think about the <u>average</u> acceleration for increasingly smaller time intervals. When the time interval is very small, the average acceleration is a good approximation to the instantaneous acceleration.

Consider a time interval Δt that begins just before the instant shown above, and ends just afterwards. (See diagram on the next page.) The speed is the same, so the lengths of the two velocity vectors are also the same. Note that the angle $\Delta \theta$ swept out by the rod during this

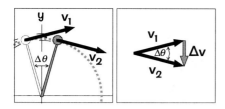

time interval is the same as the angle between the velocity vectors. This is because the velocity is perpendicular to the rod at all times. Note also that the change in velocity $\Delta \mathbf{v}$ is vertical, as shown on the near left. This means the average acceleration also is vertical.

To find the relationship for instantaneous acceleration, we will first compute the <u>average</u> acceleration for a specific case as the time interval Δt gets very small. We will use values of $R = 2$m and $v = 3$m/s throughout.

The arc length Δs is needed to determine the angle $\Delta \theta$. It is the distance traveled by the ball along the circle during time interval Δt, which is equal to $v\Delta t$. So, if the ball goes 3m/s for 1s, it covers 3m of arc along the circle. The angle $\Delta \theta$ is determined by geometry to be $\Delta \theta = \Delta s/R$. (That is, arc length $\Delta s = R\Delta \theta$.) The change in velocity $\Delta \mathbf{v}$ always points vertically down. Its magnitude is found using trigonometry to be $2v \sin(\Delta \theta/2)$. Average acceleration $\mathbf{a}_{\text{ave}}$ is found using its definition $\mathbf{a}_{\text{ave}} \equiv \Delta \mathbf{v}/\Delta t$. Note that the change in velocity is

Δt [s]	Δs [m]	$\Delta \theta$ [rad]	$\Delta \mathbf{v}$ [m/s]	$\mathbf{a}_{\text{ave}}$ [m/s^2]
1	3	1.5	4.090 ↓	4.090 ↓
0.5	1.5	0.75	2.198 ↓	4.395 ↓
0.2	0.6	0.30	0.8966 ↓	4.483 ↓
0.1	0.3	0.15	0.4496 ↓	4.496 ↓
0.05	0.15	0.075	0.2249 ↓	4.499 ↓
0.02	0.06	0.030	0.0900 ↓	4.500 ↓
0.01	0.03	0.015	0.0450 ↓	4.500 ↓

getting smaller and smaller, yet the average acceleration is approaching exactly $4^{1}/_{2}$ m/s^2.

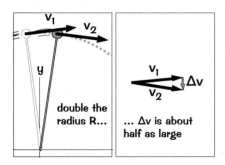

double the radius R...   ... Δv is about half as large

Keeping the time interval Δt constant, let's think about what happens to the average acceleration when we change R or v. When we double R, without changing the speed v, the distance traveled in Δt stays the same, so the angle becomes half as large, as shown on the left. This means that $\Delta \mathbf{v}$ becomes about half as large, and $\mathbf{a}_{\text{ave}}$ also is about half as large. Therefore the acceleration is proportional to $1/R$.

When we double the speed v, without changing the radius R, two changes occur. The angle doubles, because the ball is moving twice as fast, and the lengths of the velocity vectors also double, as shown to the right. This means that $\Delta \mathbf{v}$ becomes

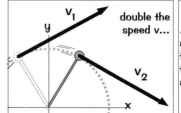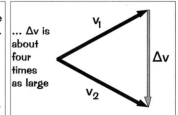

double the speed v...   ... Δv is about four times as large

about four times as large, which means that the acceleration is proportional to v^2.

Looking back to the table, we see that the average acceleration is approaching $v^2/R = 4^{1}/_{2}$ m/s^2. We conclude that the acceleration is equal to v^2/R.

So, for <u>uniform</u> circular motion, the magnitude of acceleration is <u>exactly</u>:

$$a = \frac{v^2}{R}$$

magnitude of the acceleration for uniform circular motion

The direction of the acceleration is toward the center of the circle, so it points down when the ball is on the positive y-axis, to the left when the ball is on the positive x-axis, etc. This can be verified by imagining any small time interval during the trajectory of the ball, and thinking about the change in the ball's velocity.

A ball is attached to a string and swung in a horizontal circle as shown. What is the direction of the acceleration at the instant shown?

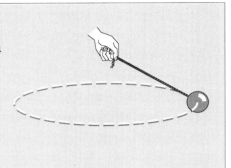

Answer. The ball is moving with constant speed, so the acceleration is towards the center of the circular path traced by the ball. At the instant shown, the direction is horizontal and to the left.

1.1.2 Newton's laws and uniform circular motion. According to Newton's 2nd law, in order to produce an acceleration, there must be a net force exerted on the object in the same direction as its acceleration. For instance, in the example above, there are only two (non-negligible) forces on the ball: gravitation pulling straight down and a tension force pulling along the string, as shown in the free-body diagram below.

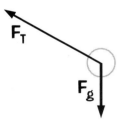

Because the acceleration is horizontal, the net force also must be horizontal. Because the net force is horizontal, the vertical component of the tension force must balance the gravitational force, and the horizontal component of the tension force is equal to the net force. In fact, because the net force is larger than the gravitational force, the acceleration is larger than 9.8m/s², even though the speed is not changing at all!

Knowing the acceleration of an object undergoing uniform circular motion often tells you something about the forces exerted on the object. For example, when a car travels around a flat curve, there must be enough friction between the tires and the road to provide the net force needed for the car to stay on the road. When the road is wet and slippery, the maximum friction force is smaller, so you must slow down to make it around the curve. In other words, you must reduce your acceleration by lowering your speed v.

1.1.3 Non-uniform circular motion. When the speed of an object is changing as it travels along a circular arc, there are two components to its acceleration: the *radial* and the *tangential*. The radial component points toward the center of the circular path (i.e., perpendicular to the direction of motion), and the tangential component points parallel to the direction of motion. For example, consider a pendulum swinging as shown below.

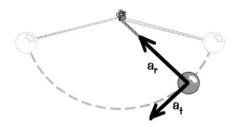

At the instant shown, there are two components of the acceleration for the ball. The radial component a_r is telling us how quickly the <u>direction</u> (of velocity) is changing, just as it did with uniform circular motion. The relationship is the same as before, because the rate at which the direction changes depends only on the speed and the radius of curvature. The only difference is that now the relationship refers only to the radial component of acceleration:

$$a_r = \frac{v^2}{R}$$

magnitude of the <u>radial component</u> of acceleration for motion along <u>any</u> circle

The direction of the radial component is again toward the center of the circular arc.

The tangential component a_t is telling us how quickly the <u>speed</u> is changing. In general:

$$a_t = \frac{\Delta v}{\Delta t} \ (\Delta t \text{ small})$$

magnitude of the <u>tangential component</u> of acceleration for motion along <u>any</u> circle

where v is the speed of the object. Because we usually do not know how the speed is changing as a function of time, this relationship is not generally useful for determining a_t. However, you can often use Newton's 2nd law to determine a_t. For instance, in the situation above, it is a component of gravitation that causes the change in speed because only gravitation has a component along the direction of motion. The direction of a_t is the same as the direction of the component of the net force parallel to the motion.

A toy car travels around a circular track as shown. At A, what force or combination of forces causes the car's (a) radial acceleration and (b) tangential acceleration? (Neglect friction and drag.)

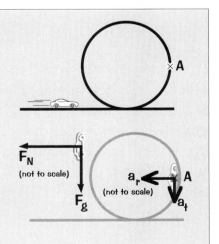

Answer. There are two non-negligible forces on the car at point A: a normal force points left, and gravitation points down. Comparing the free-body diagram to the components of acceleration, we see that (a) F_N causes the car's radial acceleration and (b) F_g causes its tangential acceleration.

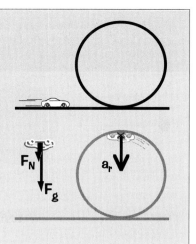

A toy car travels around a circular track as shown. At the top of the track, what force or combination of forces causes the car's (a) radial acceleration and (b) tangential acceleration? (Neglect friction and drag.)

Answer. There are two non-negligible forces on the car at the top of the track: the normal force points down and gravitation also points down. (a) Radial acceleration points down, so the sum of F_N and F_g is responsible. (b) The tangential acceleration is zero, because no forces have horizontal components.

Note that the directions of the radial and tangential components of acceleration change as an object moves around the circle.

1.1.4 Motion along a curved path. When the path of an object is not circular, we again break down the acceleration into one component perpendicular to the direction of motion and a second component parallel to the direction of motion. The trick is to find the circular arc that matches the curvature of the path at the point of interest, as shown below. Then, we use the same ideas as above: The radial component of acceleration depends on the rate at which the direction of motion is changing, and the tangential component of acceleration depends on the rate at which the speed is changing.

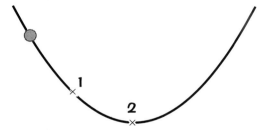

Consider a frictionless bead released from rest as shown on a parabolic wire. (This means that the wire is bent into the shape of a parabola.) To examine the acceleration of the bead at points 1 and 2, we need to find the circles that match the curvature of the wire at those same two points. Let's first consider point 1.

The dotted line shows just part of the circle that matches the curvature of the wire at point 1. (The circle is so big that we cannot show the whole circle!) The **x** indicates the center of that same circle. Note that the radial acceleration points directly towards the *center of curvature*. Note also that the tangential acceleration is in the direction of motion (rather than opposite), because the bead is speeding up due to gravitation.

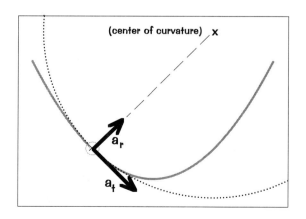

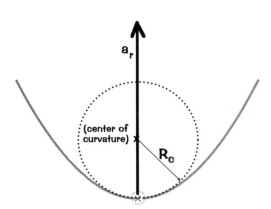

(center of curvature)

R_c

At point 2, the speed is larger than at point 1, and the *radius of curvature* R_c is smaller than at point 1, which means that the radial acceleration is much larger than at point 1. Also, because there are no forces having a horizontal component, there can be no tangential acceleration at point 2. This means the speed is not changing at that point. In other words, the speed is as large as it is going to get, and as it goes up the other side of the wire, the speed will start to decrease.

The relationship for the radial acceleration is the same as before, except we must substitute the radius of curvature R_c for the radius of the circle. Note that the relationship can still be applied to circular paths, because the radius of curvature for a circle is the radius of the circle.

$$a_r = \frac{v^2}{R_c}$$

magnitude of the <u>radial component</u> of acceleration for motion along <u>any</u> path

The direction of the radial component is toward the center of curvature.

1.1.5 Reasoning with circular motion ideas. There are really only two big new ideas in circular motion: (1) The component of an object's acceleration perpendicular to its direction of motion (that is, the *radial* component a_r) depends on the rate at which the object's <u>direction</u> is changing, and is equal to v^2/R_c, where v is the object's speed, and R_c is the *radius of curvature* of the path. (2) The component of an object's acceleration parallel to its direction of motion (the *tangential* component a_t) depends on the rate at which the object's <u>speed</u> is changing. Whether you are looking at uniform motion along a circular arc, non-uniform motion along a non-circular path, or anything in between, you can use these ideas to analyze the situation. Everything you already know about forces, free-body diagrams, empirical force laws, Newton's laws, and energy conservation can all be applied as before to these new situations.

A ball is attached to a string and released from rest when the string is horizontal. (a) What is the tension in the string just after the ball is released? (b) What is the acceleration of the ball just after it is released?

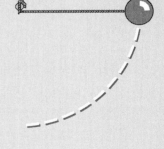

Answer. At the instant shown, the radial acceleration is to the left, and the tangential acceleration is down. At this instant, the ball is at rest, so its speed is zero. This means that the radial acceleration must be zero also. (a) Only the tension force is responsible for the radial acceleration, so the tension must be zero. (b) The only force on the ball is gravitation, so the acceleration is about 10m/s².

A free-body diagram can be useful for analyzing the forces on an object and its acceleration.

A ball is attached to a string and swings in a horizontal circle as shown. What can you say about the forces on the ball and its acceleration?

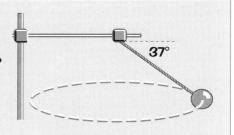

Answer. Neglecting air resistance, all forces on the ball are perpendicular to its motion, so there is no work done on the ball. Thus, the speed stays constant, which means that the magnitude of the acceleration remains constant also. Only the direction of acceleration changes, although it is horizontal at all times. This means that the net force is horizontal at all times also.

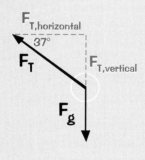

Consider the free-body diagram for the ball at the instant shown. The net force is horizontal and to the left, so the vertical component of the tension force must balance the gravitational force. Because the angle is smaller than 45°, the horizontal component of tension is larger than its vertical component. This also means that the horizontal component of tension is larger than mg, which means that the net force is larger than mg, so the acceleration is larger than 9.8m/s^2.

Note that in the example above we have used ideas covered previously about the work done by the tension and gravitational forces, about Newton's 2nd law, about the empirical force law for gravitation, and about how the tension force is exerted.

Energy ideas can be useful for determining how the speed of an object changes as it moves along its path.

A toy race car travels around a circular track as shown. Where along the circular part of the track is the radial acceleration of the car largest? Where is it smallest? (Ignore friction and drag.)

Answer. The radius of curvature is constant, so the radial acceleration depends only on the speed of the car, which is greatest at the bottom and least at the top of the track. Assuming no macroscopic energy is lost due to friction or air drag, the speed of the car is the same when it returns to the horizontal as when it started up the curved track. Therefore, the radial acceleration is largest just after the car enters the circular part of the track and again just before it exits. The radial acceleration is smallest where the speed is smallest, at the top of the track.

> **A toy race car travels around a circular track as shown. Is it possible for the car to stop at the top of the track without losing contact with the track?**
>
> *Answer.* No! There are only two forces on the car: a normal force exerted by the track pointing down, and a gravitational force also pointing down. The smallest possible net force occurs when the normal force is negligibly small, so the smallest net force is *mg*. Therefore, even at the top, there is an acceleration, which means that the car must be moving in order to stay in contact with the track. If the speed is not large enough, the car will start to travel in a parabolic path (i.e., free-fall) before it reaches the top.

1.1.6 Solving problems using circular motion ideas. You must be very flexible in your approach to solving problems involving objects traveling along curved paths. The following table lists some principles and ideas and the ways they can be useful for solving problems. It also lists some examples using the situation above involving a toy race car traveling around a circular track.

Principle / Concept	Ways to Use Principle / Concept	Examples using the situation above
Conservation of energy	• relate speed and location of object	• find the speed of a toy car at the top of a circular track
Radial acceleration ($a_r = v^2/R_c$)	• relate radial acceleration, speed, and radius of curvature	• find the radial component of acceleration for the toy car when it is halfway to the top
Newton's 2nd law ($\mathbf{F}_{net} = m\mathbf{a}$)	• relate net force, mass, and acceleration	• find the net force on the toy car just as it enters the curved part of the track • find the tangential acceleration when the car is halfway to the top
Empirical force laws ($F_g = mg$, etc.)	• relate net force and the individual forces on the object	• find the gravitational force on the toy car at any point along its trajectory
Free-body diagram	• find components of forces • identify components of forces responsible for radial and tangential accelerations	• determine the radial and tangential components of the gravitational force when the car is 3/4's of the way down the 2nd half of the track • find the normal force on the car when it is halfway up to the top

In the following example, we use almost all of these ideas to determine the normal force exerted by the track at different parts of the track.

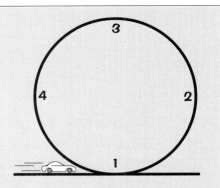

A 50g toy race car is rolling without friction on a horizontal track at 150cm/s when it enters a circular loop 14cm high. Estimate the normal force on the car at the four points indicated.

Answer. Ignoring drag and friction throughout, there are only two forces to consider: a normal force and gravitation. Because the normal force does no work on the car, the energy of the Earth–car system is constant throughout the car's motion. The following table summarizes the steps needed to determine the normal force at all four points along the path of the car.

FEATURE OF CAR [UNITS]	DEFINITION, LAW, OR PRINCIPLE	POINT ALONG CIRCULAR LOOP			
		1	2	3	4
height above ground [cm]	geometry	0.0	7.0	14.0	7.0
speed [m/s]	energy conservation	1.50	1.24	0.922	1.24
radial acceleration [m/s²]	$a_r = v^2/R_c$	32.1↑	22.1←	12.1↓	22.1→
free-body diagram	def'n of FBD	F_{N1}	F_{N2} F_g	F_{N3} F_g	F_{N4} F_g
radial comp. of net force [N]	$\mathbf{F}_{net} = m\mathbf{a}$	1.61↑	1.11←	0.61↓	1.11→
gravitational force [N]	$F_g = mg$	0.50↓	0.50↓	0.50↓	0.50↓
normal force [N]	def'n of net force	2.11↑	1.11←	0.11↓	1.11→

If you can understand how each of the values in the table above are computed, then you are well on your way to understanding how to integrate circular motion ideas into your problem-solving approach. Most variations are relatively minor compared to this problem. The individual forces may change, the path might not be along a circular arc, or you may need to use trigonometry to determine the components of forces, but the techniques and principles remain largely the same.

In the next section, we will help you to integrate *projectile motion* ideas into your problem-solving approach.

1.2 PROJECTILE MOTION

Projectile motion refers to those situations in which an object or person travels through the air subject only to the forces of gravitation and air resistance. We will find that many general features of projectile motion can be applied to other situations in which the acceleration is approximately constant.

1.2.1 Simple projectile motion. The simplest and most common example of projectile motion is when an object is thrown at relatively low speed in the air. This means that air resistance is relatively small, and the acceleration of the object is nearly constant. Consider the following strobe diagram of a boy throwing a ball into the air. The time between strobes is $1/5$ s (0.2s), so it takes about 1.6s for the ball to hit the ground (at strobe #9). Labeling the horizontal direction as x and the vertical direction as y, let's measure the location of the <u>bottom</u> of the ball at each instant and tabulate the results. Measurements are made to the nearest 2mm.

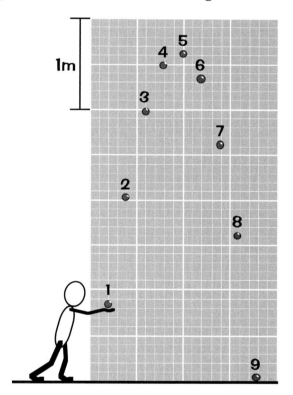

n	t	x	y	v_x	v_y
[−]	[s]	[m]	[m]	[m/s]	[m/s]
1	0.0	0.20	0.80	—	—
2	0.2	0.38	2.00	1.00	5.35
3	0.4	0.60	2.94	1.00	3.65
4	0.6	0.78	3.46	1.00	1.60
5	0.8	1.00	3.58	1.00	−0.40
6	1.0	1.18	3.30	0.95	−2.50
7	1.2	1.38	2.58	0.95	−4.35
8	1.4	1.56	1.56	1.00	−6.45
9	1.6	1.78	0.00	—	—

Note that the lower left corner of the grid is the chosen origin of the coordinate system.

The last two columns above (v_x and v_y) were computed by considering the positions of the ball immediately before and immediately after each instant. Because the time interval between strobes is relatively short, the velocity at any instant is approximately equal to the average velocity during the time interval surrounding that instant. So, for example, to find the velocity at $t = 1.2$s ($n = 7$), we use the 6th and 8th strobes. During this 0.4-second time interval, the change in x is 0.38m and the change in y is −1.74m, so the x-component of velocity (v_x) is estimated to be 0.95m/s and its y-component (v_y) is estimated to be −4.35m/s. (Note that the $n = 1$ and $n = 9$ components of velocity cannot be computed, because there is no measurement of the position before $n = 1$ or after $n = 9$.)

Plots of v_x vs. t and v_y vs. t confirm what we already know from studying dynamics: The only non-negligible force on the ball is gravitation, so the net force is in the vertical direction. This means that the acceleration of the ball is also in the vertical direction. Computing the slopes of the two straight lines below, we get the following two components of acceleration:

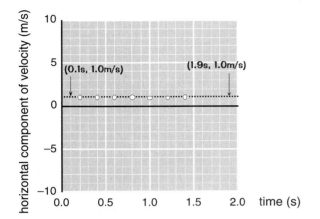

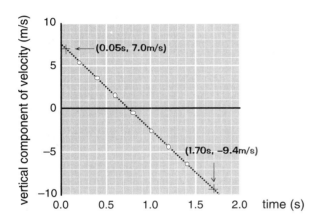

$$a_x = a_{x,\text{ave}} \equiv \frac{\Delta v_x}{\Delta t}$$

$$= \frac{1.0\text{m/s} - 1.0\text{m/s}}{1.9\text{s} - 0.1\text{s}}$$

$$= 0.0\text{m/s}^2$$

$$a_y = a_{y,\text{ave}} \equiv \frac{\Delta v_y}{\Delta t}$$

$$= \frac{-9.4\text{m/s} - 7.0\text{m/s}}{1.7\text{s} - 0.05\text{s}}$$

$$= -9.94\text{m/s}^2$$

Note that we used the straight lines—not the data points—to compute slopes. Even though there are variations in v_x, the variations are so small that the slope of v_x vs. t is zero. In the y-direction, we get a slope of about -9.9m/s^2, which is close to what we might expect for an object under the influence of gravitation only (-9.8m/s^2). Deviations are caused primarily by the data-taking process.

There is no appreciable force in the horizontal direction while the ball is traveling through the air. (The boy's hand exerted a horizontal force on the ball before letting go of it, but that force is gone as soon as he lets go of the ball.) The ball moves horizontally because it has an initial velocity in the horizontal direction. A force is not needed to keep it moving horizontally.

1.2.2 Algebraic representation of simple projectile motion. Because the acceleration in the horizontal direction is zero, a sketch of x vs. t produces a straight line, as shown to the left. The value of x at $t = 0$s is denoted x_0, and the slope of the line is the (constant) x-component of velocity v_x. The equation for this straight line gives us an algebraic expression for the x-coordinate as a function of time:

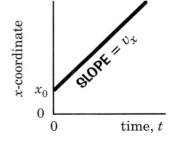

$$x(t) = x_0 + v_x t \quad \text{(constant } v_x\text{)}$$

Because the acceleration in the vertical direction is not zero, a sketch of y vs. t is curved, which does not help us to find algebraic expressions for v_y and y as functions of time. However, because a_y is constant, a sketch of v_y vs. t will help us.

The slope of v_y vs. t is the y-component of acceleration a_y, so when the acceleration is constant, the equation for the straight line shown to the right gives us an algebraic expression for v_y as a function of time:

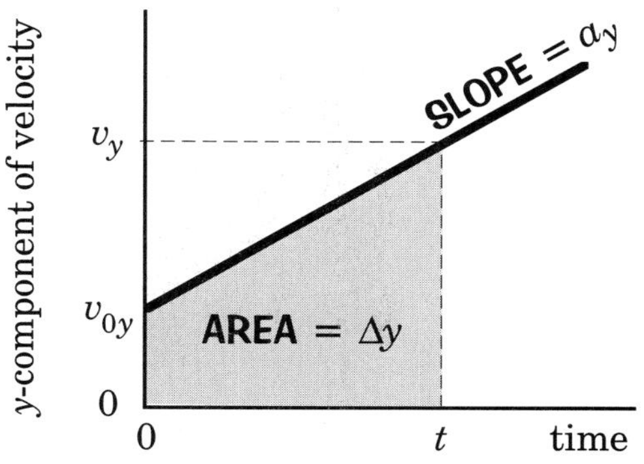

$$v_y(t) = v_{0y} + a_y t$$

where v_{0y} is the y-component of velocity at $t = 0$s.

Also, when the acceleration is constant, the area beneath the graph of v_y vs. t is Δy, the change in the object's y-coordinate. This gives us an expression for the y-coordinate as a function of time:

$$y(t) = y_0 + v_{0y}t + \tfrac{1}{2}a_y t^2$$

where y_0 is the y-coordinate of the object at $t = 0$s, and v_{0y} is again the initial value of v_y.

1.2.3 Algebraic representation of two-dimensional motion. Simple projectile motion is only one example of a wider class of situations in which objects move in two dimensions with a constant acceleration. In order to simplify and generalize the previous kinematic expressions, we define the position vector $\mathbf{r}$, the velocity vector $\mathbf{v}$, and the acceleration vector $\mathbf{a}$:

$$\mathbf{r} \equiv (x, y) \qquad \mathbf{v} \equiv (v_x, v_y) \qquad \mathbf{a} \equiv (a_x, a_y)$$

This means that the <u>initial</u> position vector is $\mathbf{r}_0 = (x_0, y_0)$ and the initial velocity vector is $\mathbf{v}_0 = (v_{0x}, v_{0y})$. Now all the kinematic expressions listed in the previous section can be summarized with just two vector equations:

$$\mathbf{r}(t) = \mathbf{r}_0 + \mathbf{v}_0 t + \tfrac{1}{2}\mathbf{a}t^2$$

$$\mathbf{v}(t) = \mathbf{v}_0 + \mathbf{a}t$$

**kinematic expressions
for position and velocity
as functions of time
for constant acceleration**

Note how similar these <u>vector</u> equations are to the equations derived for one-dimensional motion in Chapter 1 of the *Motion* Reader. However, the vector properties of these equations are very important. Consider the following way of rewriting the first vector equation above:

$$\left.\begin{array}{c} x(t) \\ y(t) \end{array}\right\} = \left\{\begin{array}{c} x_0 + v_{0x}t + \tfrac{1}{2}a_x t^2 \\ y_0 + v_{0y}t + \tfrac{1}{2}a_y t^2 \end{array}\right. \qquad \text{(constant acceleration } \mathbf{a}\text{)}$$

Note also that the expressions above (for $\mathbf{r}(t)$ and $\mathbf{v}(t)$) are valid for <u>any</u> motion during which the acceleration is constant.

1.2.4 Free-fall acceleration. Before proceeding, we need to make some comments about the similarities and differences between the gravitational constant ($g \approx 10\text{N/kg}$) and the acceleration of an object in free-fall. An object in free-fall has only one force on it: gravitation, $F_g = mg$. By Newton's 2nd law, $F_{\text{net}} = ma$. The mass m appears in both relationships, so the acceleration of every object in free-fall (i.e., ignoring all forces but gravitation) is the same: $a = g$. We notate this special "free-fall" acceleration a_g to indicate that it is an acceleration, and that it corresponds to a situation in which only gravitation is exerted on the object. Its value is equal to g, but g is a proportionality constant in an empirical force law, not an acceleration. Although the exact value of a_g is about 9.81m/s^2, for convenience, we use a value of 10m/s^2.

1.2.5 Special features of simple projectile motion. Once the initial position and velocity of a projectile are known, the entire *trajectory* is established. In other words, the position and velocity of the projectile are known for all times afterward. It is often more convenient, however, to capture the essence of a trajectory by focusing on three special features: the time of flight T, the range R, and the maximum altitude H. All three are defined assuming that the projectile travels over level ground and that its initial altitude is at ground level. A diagram of a typical trajectory is shown below.

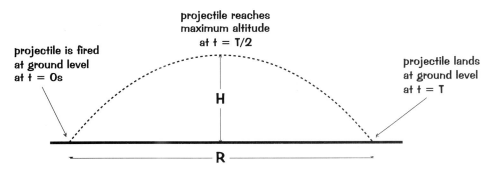

We can assume that the dotted line represents the path of a baseball, cannon ball, or any other object moving through the air. We are still ignoring air resistance.

The time of flight T is the total length of time it takes for the projectile to return to ground level after being fired. For simple projectile motion, it depends only on the <u>vertical</u> component of initial velocity (v_{0y}) and the acceleration of the projectile (a_g); it does <u>not</u> depend on the horizontal component of initial velocity (v_{0x}). In particular, the time of flight is the same for all trajectories with the same v_{0y}.

The maximum altitude H is the maximum height above the ground achieved by the projectile. Like the time of flight, it depends only on v_{0y} and a_g, and not on v_{0x}.

The range R is the horizontal distance traveled by the projectile while it is in the air. It depends on the horizontal component of initial velocity and the time of flight. (Keep in mind that v_{0x} is constant throughout the motion of the projectile, so $R = v_{0x}T$.)

1.2.6 Reasoning about simple projectile motion. Much can be deduced and learned about trajectories by analyzing and comparing them without resorting to equations.

In this first example, we begin to see some patterns in how the speed and velocity of a projectile change during a trajectory.

A baseball is thrown with an initial velocity of (6m/s, 8m/s) and follows the trajectory shown to the right. What is the baseball's smallest speed while it is in the air, and where does this occur?

Answer. The horizontal component of velocity (in this case, 6m/s) does not change during the motion of the baseball; only its vertical component changes. The vertical component of velocity is initially 8m/s, and it gets smaller and smaller until it reaches zero at the top, after which it becomes more and more negative. Because the horizontal component of velocity is constant, the speed is smallest when the vertical component of velocity is smallest: at the top. Because the vertical component is zero at this moment, the speed of the baseball is equal to its horizontal component: 6m/s.

Using the same situation, what is the velocity of the baseball (a) at the top of the trajectory, and (b) just before it hits the ground?

Answer. At both the top and the end of the trajectory, the horizontal component of the velocity is 6m/s. Its vertical component changes from 8m/s to 0m/s in going from the beginning to the top of the trajectory. By symmetry, because it takes the same amount of time to go up as it takes to come back down, the vertical component of velocity must change from 0m/s at the top to –8m/s at the end of the trajectory. (The minus sign is needed to indicate that the baseball is coming back down.) So, at the top, the velocity of the baseball is (6m/s, 0m/s), and at the end, its velocity is (6m/s, –8m/s). The diagram at left shows the velocities of the baseball at the beginning, top, and end of its trajectory.

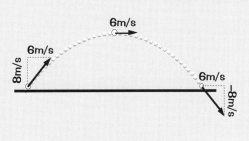

Note in the example above that we did not use any equations to determine these features of the baseball's trajectory. Also, we are using the convention defined on page R13 for velocity vectors: $\mathbf{v} = (v_x, v_y)$. In other words, the x-component of velocity is the first value and its y-component is the second value in parentheses. We are also assuming the horizontal direction is the x-direction, and the vertical direction is the y-direction.

Comparing trajectories is another useful way of distinguishing features of projectile motion, as shown in the next examples.

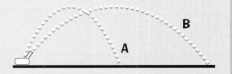

A cannon shoots two cannon balls, A and B, as shown. The maximum altitudes of both trajectories are the same, but the range of B is about twice the range of A. Which ball is in the air longer?

> *Answer.* It might appear that ball B is in the air longer because it is traveling farther, but this is not true. The maximum altitude depends only on the vertical component of initial velocity (v_{0y}) and the acceleration. The accelerations of the two balls are the same, so the vertical components of their initial velocities must be the same also. This means that the two balls spend the <u>same</u> amount of time in the air. (The reason ball B travels farther is that the horizontal component of its velocity must be larger than that of ball A.)

Which ball is moving faster just after being fired by the cannon?

> *Answer.* The y-components of initial velocity are the same, but their x-components are different. Ball B has the larger x-component, so it has the larger initial speed.

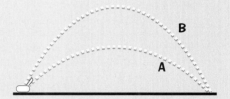

A cannon shoots two cannon balls, A and B, as shown. The ranges of both trajectories are the same, but the maximum altitude of B is about twice that of A. Which ball is traveling faster horizontally at the beginning of its trajectory?

> *Answer.* It might seem as if there is not enough information given in this situation to answer this question. The key is to realize or notice that because the two ranges are the same, the ball that spends less time in the air must be moving faster in the horizontal direction. We know that ball A spends less time in the air because its maximum altitude is smaller. Therefore, ball A is moving faster horizontally than ball B at the beginning (and at all times while they are in the air).

Which ball is moving faster just after being fired by the cannon?

> *Answer.* We cannot say if the initial speeds of the two cannon balls are the same or different. Ball A has the larger x-component of initial velocity and ball B has the larger y-component, so they might have the same speed or different speeds, and we cannot say for sure which ball is moving faster.

Newton's laws are often helpful for explaining why projectiles behave the way they do.

A baseball is thrown with an initial velocity of (6m/s, 8m/s) and follows the trajectory shown to the right. What is the direction of the net force on the baseball at the top of the trajectory?

Answer. If we ignore air resistance, the net force on the baseball is the same at all times and equal to the gravitational force on the baseball (*mg*, down). Therefore, even though the baseball is moving horizontally when it is at the top of its trajectory, the net force on the ball is pointing straight down.

Newton's 2nd law tells us that the net force is always in the same direction as the acceleration. For simple projectile motion, the net force is equal to the gravitational force, which is constant and directed downward at all times (for any particular projectile). Therefore, by Newton's 2nd law, the acceleration of any projectile is constant and directed downward at all times. This is why only the vertical component of the velocity changes and the horizontal component of velocity remains the same throughout the motion of any particular projectile.

Conservation of energy can be fruitfully applied to simple projectile motion because air resistance is being ignored and therefore the only force on the projectile is gravitation.

A baseball is thrown as shown. Which is larger for the ball, its initial or final kinetic energy?

Answer. The total energy of the system (Earth and baseball) consists of gravitational potential energy and kinetic energy of the baseball. The total energy is constant. The change in gravitational potential energy depends on the change in height for the baseball. The final height is the same as the initial height, so there is no change in U_g. Therefore, there is no difference between the initial and final kinetic energies; they are the same.

Identical balls are thrown at the same speed from the same height off identical cliffs as shown. Which ball has the largest speed when it hits? Which has the smallest?

Answer. All 4 balls have the same initial kinetic energy and the same change in kinetic energy because they all have the same mass and the same overall change in height. So, they all have the same final kinetic energy and the <u>same</u> final speed.

1.2.7 Solving problems in simple projectile motion. As a reminder, here are the two sets of relationships we are working with in this section. Keep in mind that these are derived assuming that the acceleration is constant and directed downward with a magnitude of a_g (about 10m/s^2). This means that $a_x = 0$ and $a_y = -a_g$.

$$x(t) = x_0 + v_{0x}t \qquad\qquad y(t) = y_0 + v_{0y}t - \tfrac{1}{2}a_g t^2$$
$$v_x(t) = v_{0x} \qquad\qquad v_y(t) = v_{0y} - a_g t$$

There are four keys to solving projectile motion problems. The first key is to recognize that these four kinematic expressions are not completely independent of each other. The time t is the same in all four relationships, and this ties them together. This common feature will allow you to solve many problems that otherwise might seem impossible.

The second key to solving projectile motion problems is to make sure you interpret given information carefully and translate it correctly into equation form. For example, if you are told that the altitude of a projectile is 12m at $t = 1.8$s, first define $y_1 \equiv 12$m and $t_1 \equiv 1.8$s, then write:

$$y_1 = y(t_1) = y_0 + v_{0y}t_1 - \tfrac{1}{2}a_g t_1{}^2$$

or if you prefer:

$$12\text{m} = y_0 + (v_{0y})(1.8\text{s}) - \tfrac{1}{2}(a_g)(1.8\text{s})^2$$

(This second form of this equation might seem easier to you, but in the long run, it is usually easier to rearrange symbols such as y_1 and t_1 than to rearrange values such as 12m and 1.8s.)

The only unknowns in this equation are y_0 and v_{0y}, so the given information leads directly to a relationship between these two unknowns as shown to the right. This means that there are many combinations of y_0 and v_{0y} that will cause the given observation to become true. If you know the value of either one of these, you can immediately solve for the other.

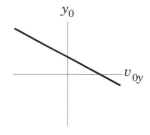

Keep in mind that often information is not explicitly given. For instance, ground level ($y = 0$m) is sometimes not given in a problem, and usually you have the freedom to define ground level to be anywhere you want. Similarly, you often have the freedom to define the initial horizontal position.

A third key is to focus on special features of trajectories, such as maximum height, time of flight, and range, and also to focus on the endpoints of the motion, such as initial and final positions and initial and final velocities. For instance, the maximum altitude is special because the y-component of velocity is zero at the same instant that the altitude is maximum.

The last key to solving projectile motion problems is to be able to recognize when you have enough equations to solve for the desired unknown. To do this, count the number of equations and the number of unknowns <u>in those equations</u>. Make sure the desired unknown is in one of your equations! If the total number of equations is equal to the total number of unknowns, then you are ready to solve them. For instance, a second bit of information might give you a second relationship between y_0 and v_{0y}, as represented in the diagram at right. The solution is the point at which the two lines intersect, and this is why you need two equations to determine two unknowns. Likewise, three equations are needed when there are three unknowns, and so on.

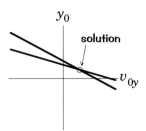

Two examples will help you to understand these four keys to solving projectile motion problems. Here's the first example.

A baseball is thrown with an initial velocity of (v_{0x}, v_{0y}) and follows the trajectory shown to the right. How long does it take before it lands again? (What is the time of flight T?)

Answer. There are actually two ways to solve this problem. The <u>harder</u> way is to use the relationship for y vs. t. We know that the height of the ball is zero at $t = 0$ and $t = T$. (This is what is meant by the time of flight.) This information gives us two equations ($y(0) = 0$ and $y(T) = 0$) and there are two unknowns (y_0 and T), so there is enough information to solve for T. Unfortunately, solving these equations is slightly more difficult due to the t^2 term in $y(t)$.

The easier way to solve this problem is to use velocity. We know that it takes the same amount of time to reach the maximum height as it does to come back down. We also know that the vertical component of velocity must be zero at the topmost point in the trajectory. Therefore, we have one equation and one unknown.

The one equation is:

$$v_y(t = T/2) = 0$$

In other words, the y-component of velocity (v_y) halfway through the trajectory ($t = T/2$) is equal to zero. Now we use the kinematic expression for $v_y(t)$:

$$v_{0y} - (a_g)(T/2) = 0$$

and solve for T:

$$T = \frac{2v_{0y}}{a_g}$$

This means that the time it takes for something to reach its maximum height or the time it takes for something to return to level ground does <u>not</u> depend on the horizontal component of velocity (v_{0x}). Note the value of focusing on the endpoints of the trajectory (for the "hard" solution) and on the maximum height (for the "easier" solution).

A baseball is thrown off a cliff from a height of 3.6m above level ground with an initial velocity of (6m/s, 8m/s). (a) Where does the ball land, and (b) how fast is it moving when it lands?

Answer. Assuming the initial position of the ball is (0.0m, 3.6m), and recognizing that the horizontal velocity is constant, unknowns are the final horizontal position (x_f) and the final vertical velocity (v_{fy}). It is useful in this case to introduce a third unknown: the time at which the ball lands (t_f), because this will help us to relate the various equations. To answer part (b), we will use the Pythagorean theorem to find the final speed using the horizontal and vertical components of velocity.

There are three equations to solve:

$$x(t_f) = x_f$$
$$y(t_f) = 0$$
$$v_y(t_f) = v_{fy}$$

and there are three unknowns. Using the kinematic expressions for x, y, and v_y, we get:

$$x_0 + v_{0x}t_f = x_f$$
$$y_0 + v_{0y}t_f - \tfrac{1}{2}a_g t_f^2 = 0$$
$$v_{0y} - a_g t_f = v_{fy}$$

The 2nd equation can be immediately solved for t_f: $t_f = \dfrac{1}{a_g}\left(v_{0y} \pm \sqrt{v_{0y}^2 + 2a_g y_0}\right)$

Using $a_g = 10\text{m/s}^2$, $v_{0y} = 8\text{m/s}$, and $y_0 = 3.6\text{m}$, we get: $t_f = 1.966\text{s}$ and -0.366s

The positive root can now be inserted into the other two equations to solve for the other two unknowns (see comment below):

$$x_f = 0.0\text{m} + (6\text{m/s})(1.966\text{s})$$
$$= 11.8\text{m}$$
$$v_{fy} = 8\text{m/s} - (10\text{m/s}^2)(1.966\text{s})$$
$$= -11.66\text{m/s}$$

The horizontal velocity is constant at 6m/s, giving a final speed of 13.11m/s. So, the ball lands about 12m from the base of the cliff with a speed of about 13m/s.

Solving a quadratic equation always gives two roots. In this case, the negative root can be discarded because it does not fit the constraints of the situation, namely, that the ball is not moving at $t < 0$s, so the equations are only valid for $t \geq 0$s. Also, an additional unknown (t_f) was introduced to make the problem easier to solve. This instant of time ties together all the equations. Finally, we defined the initial horizontal position of the ball to be 0.0m, and we defined its initial height to be 3.6m, which meant that the ball landed at $y = 0$m. However, the final answers do not depend on where you choose the origin of the coordinate system to be. In other words, for any chosen origin, the ball lands 12m from the base of the cliff at 13m/s.

1.2.8 Solving problems in two-dimensional motion. Solving two-dimensional motion problems is only slightly more difficult than solving projectile motion problems. The major differences are: (1) there can be an acceleration in the x-direction; (2) the acceleration in the y-direction is not necessarily $-a_g$; and (3) you might need to determine the acceleration yourself, for instance, using Newton's laws.

The kinematic relations we will apply in this section are:

$$x(t) = x_0 + v_{0x}t + \frac{1}{2}a_x t^2 \qquad y(t) = y_0 + v_{0y}t + \frac{1}{2}a_y t^2$$
$$v_x(t) = v_{0x} + a_x t \qquad\qquad v_y(t) = v_{0y} + a_y t$$

Note how similar in structure these two sets of relations are. Keep in mind that they are valid <u>only</u> when the acceleration is constant.

The space shuttle is drifting at an angle as shown with a constant speed of 120m/s when the pilot decides to fire the engines. This produces an acceleration of 5m/s^2 in the direction the shuttle is pointed. How long should the engines be fired so that the new direction of motion is perpendicular to its original direction of motion?

Answer. The hardest part of this problem is determining the components of the shuttle's acceleration. The orientation of the shuttle can be measured to be about 53° relative to the direction of motion, so the acceleration is the hypotenuse of a 3-4-5 triangle. (See diagram.)

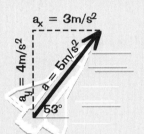

The shuttle's initial velocity is in the negative x-direction: $(v_{0x}, v_{0y}) = (-120\text{m/s}, 0\text{m/s})$. The time period ends when the velocity is in the y-direction (i.e., "perpendicular to its current direction of motion"), which means that the x-component of velocity must be zero. This occurs at $t = 40$s, so the engines should be fired for 40 seconds.

At the end of this time period, (a) how fast is the shuttle moving, (b) what direction is the shuttle pointed, and (c) what is the shuttle's position?

Answer. After 40 seconds, the new velocity is (0m/s, 160m/s), so the new speed is 160m/s. The orientation of the shuttle has not changed; it is still directed as shown, because the forces on the shuttle change only its velocity. The exact position cannot be determined, because we do not know the initial position, but the <u>change</u> in position can still be found by evaluating $x(t)$ and $y(t)$ at $t = 40$s. Note that $\Delta x = x - x_0$ and $\Delta y = y - y_0$, so after 40 seconds, $\Delta x = -2400$m and $\Delta y = 3200$m.

In the previous example, even though the acceleration has a positive x-component, the change in x is negative because the x-component of velocity is negative during the entire time period. In the next example, we use two-dimensional motion ideas to simplify the problem.

A rock is thrown horizontally off the side of a large hill at about 20m/s. Where does the rock land, and how fast is it moving when it lands?

Answer. This problem could be solved using simple projectile motion, but the hill makes it particularly hard. To make the problem easier, we use a rotated coordinate system in which x is measured along the hill, and y is measured perpendicular to the hill. This means that the initial velocity of the rock now has both an x- and a y-component, and although the acceleration still points "down", in this coordinate system it has two components also. (See diagram below.)

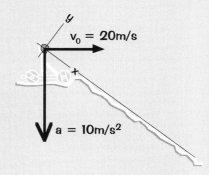

The initial position is chosen to be $(x_0, y_0) = (0\text{m}, 0\text{m})$. The hill is at an angle of $37°$, so the initial velocity is $(v_{0x}, v_{0y}) = (16\text{m/s}, 12\text{m/s})$, and the acceleration is constant at $(a_x, a_y) = (6\text{m/s}^2, -8\text{m/s}^2)$. Now we are ready to solve the problem.

The maximum value of y (in the rotated coordinate system) occurs when $v_y = 0$, which occurs at $t = 1.5\text{s}$. Because the initial and final values of y are the same, it takes another 1.5s for the rock to land, for a total of 3 seconds. To determine where the rock lands, we evaluate $x(t)$ at $t = 3\text{s}$, which is 75m. In other words, the rock lands about 75m from where it is launched as measured along the hill.

The final speed is found by evaluating $v_x(t)$ and $v_y(t)$ at $t = 3\text{s}$, and then using these components in the Pythagorean theorem. So, the final velocity is $(34\text{m/s}, -12\text{m/s})$ for a final speed of about 36m/s.

Note that time at which the rock lands could also be found by solving the equation $y(t) = 0$. There are two roots: $t_1 = 0$ and $t_2 = -2v_{0y}/a_y$. The first root represents the given information that the rock is at $y = 0$ at $t = 0$. The second root is the time at which the rock lands, $t_2 = 3\text{s}$. Also, because there is an acceleration in the x-direction, the x-component of final velocity (34m/s) is different from the x-component of initial velocity (16m/s).

We have completed projectile motion and we have shown how the basic ideas apply to all two-dimensional motion having constant acceleration. In the next section, we will study *relative motion*, and we will see how descriptions and explanations of motion can be very different when viewed from different perspectives.

1.3 RELATIVE MOTION

Relative motion refers to those situations and problems in which two objects or people are moving relative to each other. You will find that it is sometimes useful to view the motion of something from different perspectives in order to gain deeper insight into the physical principles involved. Further, you will find that the descriptions of motion might be different when observed from different perspectives, but in certain cases, the laws of physics as you have learned them remain valid and applicable.

We often ignore certain features of a situation. For instance, when analyzing the motion of people and objects on the Earth, we usually ignore the spinning of the Earth. We assume that the "ground" is at rest, but actually it is moving rather quickly (as much as 1000mph!). Because the Earth is orbiting the Sun, the Earth is moving more than 60,000mph relative to the Sun. Until now, you have ignored the motion of the ground relative to the center of the Earth, and also the motion of the Earth relative to the Sun, but you probably did not realize it. In this section you will learn why you can ignore these features, and you will learn how to decide when to ignore them.

1.3.1 Relative motion in one dimension. Imagine that you are at an airport or other large-scale public transportation terminal with a "moving sidewalk" or "moving walkway". A fixed camera is mounted on the ceiling above the moving walkway, which allows us to look at the motion of four people who are currently located near each other.

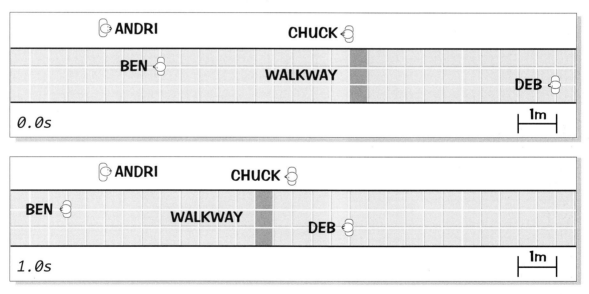

Andri is standing next to the walkway. We know this because her position has not changed. Ben moves 2¹/₂m to the left, but so does the walkway, as shown by the movement of the gray strip. This means that Ben is standing on the walkway. Chuck moves 1¹/₂m to the left, and Deb moves 5¹/₂m to the left during the time interval shown. But Deb moves only 3m closer to the gray strip on the walkway.

Assuming everyone is moving with constant velocity, we can use average velocity to determine everyone's velocity. There are two perspectives here: from the ground and from the walkway. The table below shows what each person's velocity is from both perspectives. (Minus signs are used to indicate motion to the left, and plus signs indicate motion to the right.)

table of velocities (in m/s)
as seen from two perspectives

as seen from...	Andri	Ben	Chuck	Deb
... the ground	0	$-2^{1}/_{2}$	$-1^{1}/_{2}$	$-5^{1}/_{2}$
... the walkway	$2^{1}/_{2}$	0	+1	−3

Even though Ben is not moving relative to the walkway, an observer on the ground would determine that he is moving to the left at $2^{1}/_{2}$ m/s. And even though Chuck is moving to the left relative to the ground, an observer on the walkway would determine that he is moving to the right.

1.3.2 Reference frames. One way to help you to understand and organize relative motion ideas is to use reference frames. A *reference frame* is an origin and a set of coordinate axes (for instance, x, y, and z). The ground and the walkway each defines a reference frame. For now we ignore the y- and z-directions, and for convenience we assume that the positive x-direction is to the right for both frames. Let's re-draw the first photograph from before, this time with reference frame information on it.

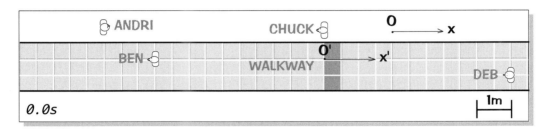

The origin of the ground's frame is denoted O, and positions are denoted x. Positive x is to the right. The origin of the walkway's frame is denoted O', and positions are denoted x'. Positive x' is to the right, even though the walkway is moving to the left (relative to frame O). The table below shows the positions in both frames of all four people at $t = 0.0$s.

Each position measured in O is different than each position measured in O' by 2m because the two origins are separated by 2m (horizontally) at $t = 0.0$s.

table of positions (in m)
as measured in two frames at $t = 0.0$s

	Andri	Ben	Chuck	Deb
O	$-8^{1}/_{2}$	−7	−2	$+3^{1}/_{2}$
O'	$-6^{1}/_{2}$	−5	0	$+5^{1}/_{2}$

At a later time, some of these positions change. The only positions that do <u>not</u> change are Andri's position measured in O, and Ben's position measured in O'.

Note that the origin of frame O' is moving relative to the origin of frame O, so even though Andri is not moving relative to O, her position in O' is changing.

1.3.3 Notation and language. You may have noticed that we have placed a "prime" (′) next to some symbols and not next to others. When you have more than one reference frame, you need some way of distinguishing them. In this example, we assigned the ground to be the "unprimed" frame, so all velocities measured relative to the ground have no additional symbol. We assigned the walkway to be the "primed" frame, so all velocities measured relative to the walkway have the additional symbol. Here is the first photograph again, this time with velocity information added to it.

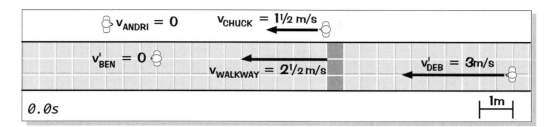

So, for instance, Chuck's speed is labeled v_{CHUCK} (that is, without a "prime") because his speed is measured relative to the ground, and Deb's speed is labeled v'_{DEB} because her speed is measured relative to the walkway.

Getting used to the language of relative motion is one of the hardest parts of this subject. For instance, in the frame of the walkway, we write $v'_{WALKWAY} = 0$ and $v'_{BEN} = 0$, because they are not moving "relative" to frame O', yet everyone would agree—even Ben!—that he and the walkway are moving. What is going on here?

Part of the answer lies in our experience. Our most familiar reference frame is the ground, and we usually treat the ground as a preferred reference frame, because it is "fixed". We do not have as much experience in reference frames moving relative to the ground, so we might be reluctant to use these other frames to describe and explain the motion or behavior of objects and people.

Another part of the answer lies in our perceptions. When you are in a car driving down the road, you <u>could</u> imagine that you not moving and that the road, trees, signs, etc. are moving past you, but that does not change what is moving and what is fixed. Also, vibrations cause tiny changes to an otherwise constant velocity. We perceive these accelerations and associate them with motion relative to the Earth, whether we are in a car, on a train, or in an elevator. Imagine that you are stopped at a traffic light, and out of the corner of your eye, you notice that the car next to you starts to move slowly. Your first impression is most likely to be that you are moving, not the other car, even though you are at rest the whole time. The combination of vibrations and visual cues have led you to perceive motion when there is none. When these are missing, there is no way for you to tell that you are moving, and thus, there is no preferred reference frame for describing the motion of something.

1.3.4 Relative motion in two dimensions. Let's consider a more complicated situation. Suppose that Jamal is riding his skateboard at 5m/s and throws a ball straight up into the air, so that he can catch it again a little later. Below is a strobe diagram showing how this situation appears to Betty, who is watching this process while standing on the ground near Jamal.

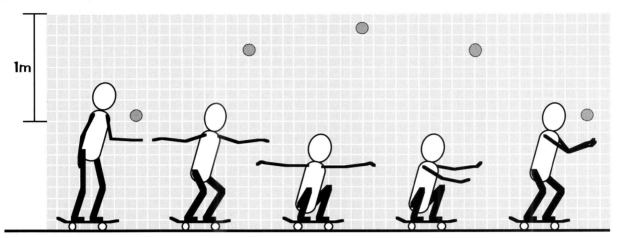

To Jamal, the motion of the ball is one-dimensional—he sees the ball go straight up and straight down, with the ball always just in front of him; the ball's velocity is vertical at all times. In other words, in Jamal's reference frame, only the vertical position of the ball is changing; the horizontal position remains the same, so the velocity is vertical at all times. To Betty, the motion of the ball is two-dimensional; the ball's initial velocity has both a horizontal and vertical component. In particular, both the ball and Jamal move at 5m/s to the right during the entire process. In other words, in Betty's frame of reference, both the vertical and horizontal position of the ball is changing, and so, the velocity of the ball has both vertical and horizontal components.

1.3.5 Position and velocity transformations. Here is where the notation described in section 1.3.3 becomes particularly useful. Consider the situation shown at right. Sue is walking along a path at 3m/s relative to the ground. A boat is traveling at 6m/s relative to a river flowing at 4m/s relative to the ground. The origin O and the two coordinate axes x and y represent the ground's reference frame. The origin O' and the two coordinate axes x' and y' represent the river's reference frame. We would like to derive and understand the relationships needed to transform the position and velocity of something in one frame to its position and velocity in another frame.

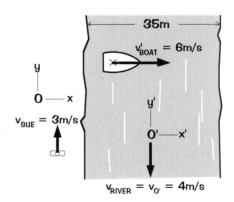

We start with a graphical representation (see diagram on the next page). At the instant shown, the position of the boat as measured in frame O is represented by the arrow (directed line segment) labeled $\mathbf{r}_{BOAT}$. The position of the boat as measured in frame O' is represented by the arrow labeled $\mathbf{r}'_{\text{BOAT}}$. In order to transform from one reference frame to the other, we need to use the position of the origin of frame O' as measured in frame O ($\mathbf{r}_{O'}$ in the diagram). Recalling the rules for adding vectors, we can see that $\mathbf{r}_{\text{BOAT}}$ is the vector sum of $\mathbf{r}_{O'}$ and $\mathbf{r}'_{\text{BOAT}}$.

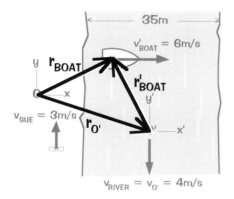

Numerically and symbolically, this same transformation is shown below. (We have used 1cm = 10m as the scale of the drawing.)

$$\begin{array}{rr} (30\text{m}, & -10\text{m}) \\ + (-10\text{m}, & 20\text{m}) \\ \hline (20\text{m}, & 10\text{m}) \end{array} \qquad \begin{array}{c} \mathbf{r}_{O'} \\ + \ \mathbf{r}'_{\text{BOAT}} \\ \hline \mathbf{r}_{\text{BOAT}} \end{array}$$

This means that we can write a general expression for transforming the position of any object or person from one frame to another:

$$\mathbf{r} = \mathbf{r}_{O'} + \mathbf{r}' \qquad \text{position transformation from } O' \text{ to } O$$

where $\mathbf{r}$ is the position of something in the "unprimed" frame (O), $\mathbf{r}'$ is its position in the "primed" frame (O'), and $\mathbf{r}_{O'}$ is the position of the origin of frame O' as measured in frame O.

To transform from the unprimed frame to the primed frame, we use the exact same form:

$$\mathbf{r}' = \mathbf{r}'_O + \mathbf{r} \qquad \text{position transformation from } O \text{ to } O'$$

Note that we use the location of origin O as measured relative to origin O' to complete this transformation. Using Sue as an example, we get the following numerical result at the instant shown in the diagram above. Relative to origin O, Sue is located at $\mathbf{r}_{\text{SUE}} = (5\text{m}, -15\text{m})$. Relative to origin O', origin O is located at $\mathbf{r}'_O = (-30\text{m}, 10\text{m})$, so Sue's position (relative to O') is $\mathbf{r}'_{\text{SUE}} = \mathbf{r}'_O + \mathbf{r}_{\text{SUE}} = (-25\text{m}, -5\text{m})$, which can be verified using the original diagram.

Because velocity is defined to be the rate at which the position is changing, we can immediately write down vector equations for velocity transformations:

$$\mathbf{v} = \mathbf{v}_{O'} + \mathbf{v}' \qquad \text{velocity transformation from } O' \text{ to } O$$

For example, because the velocity of the boat is given relative to the river (frame O'), we use this form to find the velocity of the boat in frame O ($\mathbf{v}_{\text{BOAT}}$). In particular, it is equal to the velocity of frame O' ($\mathbf{v}_{O'}$) added to the velocity of the boat in frame O' ($\mathbf{v}'_{\text{BOAT}}$). Below are shown the velocity transformation for the boat displayed graphically (on the left), numerically (in the middle) and symbolically (on the right).

$$\begin{array}{rr} (0\text{m/s}, & -4\text{m/s}) \\ + (6\text{m/s}, & 0\text{m/s}) \\ \hline (6\text{m/s}, & -4\text{m/s}) \end{array} \qquad \begin{array}{c} \mathbf{v}_{O'} \\ + \ \mathbf{v}'_{\text{BOAT}} \\ \hline \mathbf{v}_{\text{BOAT}} \end{array}$$

Transforming from the unprimed frame has the exact same form:

$$\mathbf{v}' \;=\; \mathbf{v}'_O + \mathbf{v} \qquad\qquad \text{velocity transformation from } O \text{ to } O'$$

where we use the velocity of O relative to O'. For Sue, it is most convenient to use this form, because we are given her velocity relative to the ground (frame O):

$$\mathbf{v}'_{\text{SUE}} \;=\; \mathbf{v}'_O + \mathbf{v}_{\text{SUE}}$$

Sue's velocity in frame O' is equal to the vector sum of the velocity of frame O in O' and Sue's velocity in O. Mathematically, we find $\mathbf{v}'_{\text{SUE}} = (0\text{m/s}, 4\text{m/s}) + (0\text{m/s}, 3\text{m/s}) = (0\text{m/s}, 7\text{m/s})$. This means she is moving at 7m/s in the positive y-direction relative to the river. Note that the velocity of frame O as measured in frame O' is in the positive y-direction.

Because acceleration is the rate at which velocity is changing, we can transform accelerations:

$$\mathbf{a}' \;=\; \mathbf{a}'_O + \mathbf{a} \qquad\qquad \text{acceleration transformation from } O \text{ to } O'$$

This means that when the acceleration of one frame relative to the other is zero ($\mathbf{a}'_O$ or $\mathbf{a}_{O'}$) then the accelerations as observed in either frame are the same. Mathematically, $\mathbf{a} = \mathbf{a}'$.

Two examples will help solidify these ideas and their interconnections.

In the situation above, what is Sue's velocity relative to someone sitting on the boat?

> *Answer.* The boat can be considered a third frame of reference O'', which is moving with velocity $\mathbf{v}_{O''} = (6\text{m/s}, -4\text{m/s})$ relative to the ground (frame O). However, we need to know the velocity of frame O relative to frame O''. This velocity is $\mathbf{v}''_O = -\mathbf{v}_{O''} = (-6\text{m/s}, 4\text{m/s})$ relative to someone on the boat. Sue has a velocity of $\mathbf{v}_{\text{SUE}} = (0\text{m/s}, 3\text{m/s})$ relative to the ground, so she has a velocity $\mathbf{v}''_{\text{SUE}} = (-6\text{m/s}, 7\text{m/s})$ relative to someone on the boat. In other words, she appears to be moving in the negative x-direction and positive y-direction.

A cannon shoots a ball at 10m/s at an angle of 53° above the horizontal as shown. The cannon is mounted on a railroad car that is pulled at a constant speed of 15m/s. What is the initial velocity of the ball as seen from the ground?

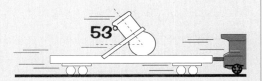

> *Answer.* The initial velocity of the ball relative to the train is $\mathbf{v}'_{\text{BALL}} = (-6\text{m/s}, 8\text{m/s})$ and the velocity of the train relative to the ground is $\mathbf{v}_{\text{TRAIN}} = \mathbf{v}_{O'} = (15\text{m/s}, 0\text{m/s})$, so the velocity of the ball relative to the ground is $\mathbf{v}_{\text{BALL}} = \mathbf{v}_{O'} + \mathbf{v}'_{\text{BALL}} = (9\text{m/s}, 8\text{m/s})$.

The ball moves to the right as it goes up into the air, even though the cannon is pointed to the left. Also, the speed of the ball in the air is larger than if the cannon were fired on the ground. (Mathematically, $v_{\text{BALL}} = \sqrt{(9\text{m/s})^2 + (8\text{m/s})^2} \approx 12\text{m/s} > 10\text{m/s}$.)

1.3.6 Newton's laws in different reference frames. Imagine that you and some of your classmates are on a train doing some science investigations. For instance, you have a heavy cart on a table attached to a horizontal spring whose other end is attached to the wall of the train. (See below.) There is a ball hanging from a piece of string attached to the ceiling, and someone is dropping a ball onto the floor of the train. Looking outside, you see a person moving to the left, about to drop an identical ball onto the ground.

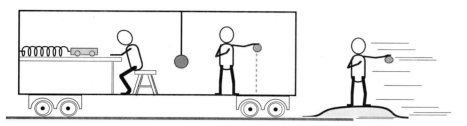

(science experiments on a train moving at constant velocity relative to the ground)

The train can be considered a reference frame moving relative to the ground. In this example, the train is moving to the right relative to the ground, so the tracks and someone on the ground appear to be moving to the left. If the train moves with constant velocity, anything you do in this frame will confirm Newton's laws of motion. For instance, when the ball is dropped, it falls straight down, and the time it takes for it to land on the floor is the same as when the ball is dropped on the ground. The ball and string hang straight down, and if you measured the tension in the string, you would get the weight of the ball. The cart would remain at rest with the spring unstretched. In other words, the laws of physics you learned from the ground's reference frame are verified inside the train moving with constant velocity.

Also, when you observe the person outside the train dropping a ball, you would see the ball travel along a parabolic path, even though the person on the ground sees it fall straight down. Thus the description of the motion is very different for you (from the train) than for the other person (on the ground). However, your measurements would yield some of the same results: you would conclude that the acceleration of the ball is constant and equal to the value you determined for the ball dropped inside the train. Only the positions and velocities in the two frames are different; the forces and the accelerations are the same.

This picture changes dramatically when the train (i.e., your reference frame) is accelerating. Let's assume the train is slowing down, which means that the tracks and the person standing on the ground appear to be slowing down relative to the train. (See diagram below.) Now, when the ball is dropped from inside the train it moves horizontally as it falls. (Note that the path is still a straight line as perceived in this accelerating frame.) The time it takes to fall is the same, but the measured acceleration is larger than expected. The ball and string now hang at an angle, and the tension in the string is no longer equal to the weight of the ball (as measured on the ground). Finally, the spring attached to the cart is stretched, even though the cart is at rest, indicating that there is a net force on the cart.

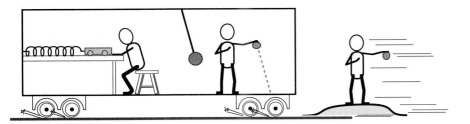

(science experiments on a train slowing down relative to the ground)

In this accelerating frame, Newton's laws and the empirical force laws, as you have learned them, do not apply. In this frame, objects appear to have an additional force exerted on them. This is how someone on the train can tell if they are in an accelerating reference frame.

Even when we seem to be at rest—standing in the hallway, sitting in class, eating lunch with friends—we are actually moving very quickly, literally hurtling through space at more than 60,000 miles per hour (relative to the Sun). Because the Earth is traveling in a circle around the Sun, it has an acceleration. This acceleration (relative to the Sun) is non-zero but very small—about 0.006m/s^2. Most experiments on the Earth are not sensitive enough to detect deviations from Newton's laws caused by this acceleration.

The Earth is also spinning on its axis. Relative to the center of the Earth, someone at the equator is moving at about 1000 miles per hour. But motion is not what causes deviations from Newton's laws, acceleration is, and the acceleration of someone at the equator is about $1/30 \text{m/s}^2$. This acceleration is also small, but large enough to detect in certain experiments.

We define an *inertial frame* to be a frame in which Newton's laws of motion are valid. Newton's laws are valid in all reference frames that are moving with constant velocity relative to an inertial frame. Note that even though the position and velocity of an object depend on the frame of reference, the acceleration of something is the same in all inertial frames. Because the acceleration of the surface of the Earth is so small, for many applications, we consider the surface of the Earth an inertial frame.

1.3.7 Conservation of energy in different reference frames. Imagine that you are throwing a ball. Its mass is 200g and you throw it with a speed of 20m/s, giving it a kinetic energy of 40J. This means that you have converted 40J of microscopic energy (for instance, in the form of stored chemical energy in your body) into kinetic energy of the ball. Now repeat this process on a train moving with a constant velocity of 50m/s (about 110mph). In your reference frame (inside a cabin on the train), the change in kinetic energy is again 40J, and you conclude that 40J of microscopic energy is (again) converted into kinetic energy. You also conclude that it is equally easy to throw a ball on a train as it is on the ground. In addition, the direction that you throw the ball does not affect how much energy is transferred; it is 40J when you throw it in any direction.

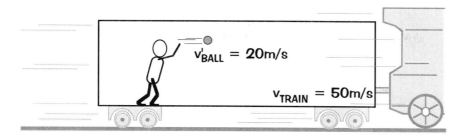

(throwing a ball in the "forward" direction from inside a moving cabin)

Now view this process from the ground's frame. The system (cabin, you, and ball) is moving at 50m/s, and the ball (at rest in your reference frame) has a kinetic energy of 250J. After you throw the ball "forward", the ball moves at 70m/s and has a kinetic energy of 490J, or 240J more than it did before! (And when you throw the ball "backward", the ball moves at 30m/s afterward and has a kinetic energy of 90J, or 160J <u>less</u> than it did before!) Your microscopic energy decreases by only 40J. How, then, does the ball gain 240J of kinetic energy?

There is nothing wrong with the law of conservation of energy. The only mistake is that we have not considered all forms of energy relevant for the ground's frame of reference. In particular, while you are throwing the ball, you exert a static friction force on the floor of the cabin. Unless something keeps the cabin moving at constant velocity, it will slow down as a result of this force. This "something" is the locomotive, and the amount of work it does on the cabin while you are throwing the ball is 200J. This means that of the 240J of energy gained by the ball, 40J comes from you and 200J comes from the locomotive.

The 40J of microscopic energy converted by you to throw the ball is the same in all frames. In your frame (inside the cabin) the locomotive does no work on the cabin, because the force is exerted through zero displacement. The following table summarizes how energy is conserved in the four scenarios mentioned in this section.

Scenario	Reference frame	Initial speed [m/s]	Final speed [m/s]	(ball's) ΔE_K [J]	(your) ΔE_{micro} [J]	Work done by external forces [J]
throw ball on ground	ground	0	20	40	−40	0
throw ball on train (any direction)	train	0	20	40	−40	0
throw ball "forward" on train	ground	50	70	240	−40	200
throw ball "backward" on train	ground	50	30	−160	−40	−200

In each case, and therefore in all frames, the work done by external forces is equal to the change in total energy of the system ($W_{ext} = \Delta E_K + \Delta E_{micro}$; $\Delta U = 0$). This is the Work–Energy Theorem, a way to apply the law of conservation of energy.

1.3.8 Reasoning with relative motion ideas. There are three major new ideas in relative motion:

- *The **reference frame** is the key to determining positions, velocities, and energy.* So, when describing the motion of objects and when applying conservation of energy, we must be very careful to indicate the frame, because descriptions can be different in different frames.

- *On the other hand, forces, masses, and accelerations are independent of reference frame, as long as the frame is **inertial**.* So, when applying Newton's laws, we must make sure that the frame is not accelerating (relative to an inertial frame). Even though the surface of the Earth is accelerating relative to the Sun, the surface is still considered an inertial frame, because the acceleration is so small.

- *There is **no preferred** inertial frame of reference.* Since physical laws and principles are equally valid in any inertial frame, all inertial frames are equally valid for describing the behavior of objects, for analyzing the forces, momentum, or energy in a system, or for solving a problem. This means we must give up the idea of an "absolute" rest frame, because there is no way to use the laws of physics to distinguish different inertial frames. They are all equivalent.

Even though there is no preferred inertial frame, there are times when a problem or situation is easier to analyze within one frame than another. This means we must think about which frame (or frames) to use when reasoning or solving problems.

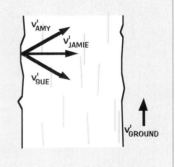

Amy, Jamie, and Sue are attempting to cross a river. All three are strong swimmers, and all three can swim at a steady rate of 3mph in still water. Amy says that the best way to cross the river is to head upstream, so that your velocity (as seen from the ground) is directed straight toward the other side. Jamie says that the best way is to head straight across even though this will take you downstream. Sue says the best way is to head downstream so that your speed is larger. Which girl is correct, and why?

> *Answer.* First we must decide exactly what is meant by "the best way." If the goal is to land directly across from the starting point, then Amy is correct. However, if the goal is to get across in the least amount of time, then Jamie is correct.
>
> There are five reference frames to consider in this situation—one for each of the girls, one for the ground, and one for the river—but only the last two are useful for answering this question. Let's look at each of the goals separately and see why there are different answers and different explanations.

(continued)

Answer (continued).

<u>Goal 1: Go directly to the other side.</u> To view this situation in the ground's frame, each velocity must be transformed (as shown to the right). In this frame, only Amy is moving horizontally, so only she will get to the other side directly across from the starting point. Jamie and Sue are carried downstream by the current.

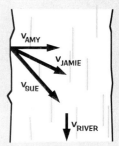

<u>Goal 2. Get to the other side in the least time.</u> To determine which girl is correct we can use either frame. All three girls have the same horizontal distance to travel. Therefore, in the ground's frame, the girl with the largest horizontal component of velocity gets to the other side the quickest. This is Jamie, although it is difficult to see in this frame.

It is a little easier to view this process in the river's frame. (Use the original drawing, with velocities shown relative to the river.) The river has a uniform width, and all three girls have the same speed, so Jamie, who swims straight across the river, will get to the other side soonest, even though she will be carried downstream by the river and will travel a longer distance than Amy relative to the ground.

Of Amy and Sue, which girl gets to the other side sooner?

Answer. It might appear that because Sue is traveling faster than Amy (relative to the ground) she will arrive sooner than Amy. However, she must travel a longer distance, so it is difficult to tell which girl reaches the other side first. The ground's frame is not the most useful frame for analyzing this situation. The river's frame is better. Relative to the river, both girls are swimming at an angle, the same angle relative to the horizontal. They both have the same distance to travel, and they both have the same speed, so they will both reach the other side at the same time.

Amy travels the least distance relative to the ground, but takes longer than Jamie to get to the other side. Jamie travels farther than Amy (again relative to the ground), but reaches the other side in the least time. Sue travels the fastest relative to the ground, but also travels the longest distance, and gets to the other side at the same time as Amy.

1.3.9 Solving problems with relative motion ideas. Solving problems in relative motion is not that different than analyzing and reasoning. The only difference is that once you have determined which frame is best for understanding the situation, you must decide which equations are needed and then solve those equations for the desired unknown.

Some of the most common problems in relative motion involve navigation. In other words, what direction should you point a plane or boat so that you reach your destination in the least amount of time? An example is shown on the next page.

A small airplane flies at 200mph in still air. On a particular flight, the destination is 150mi to the east and there is a northerly wind of 50mph. Normally it would take about 45min to reach the other airport. Due to the wind, will it take longer, shorter, or the same amount of time?

Answer. The ground is chosen to be the unprimed frame O, and the air is chosen to be the primed frame O'. A northerly wind points south, so the velocity of the air in the unprimed frame points south as shown.

The destination is east of the starting point, so the velocity of the plane in the ground's frame ($\mathbf{v}_{PLANE}$) must point east also. This means that the velocity of the plane in the air's frame ($\mathbf{v}'_{PLANE}$) must point slightly north. The length of the arrow is smaller for the plane's velocity relative to the ground, so the speed of the plane relative to the ground is less than 200mph. This means that due to the wind, it must take longer than 45 minutes to reach the other airport.

What direction should the plane fly to reach its destination?

Answer. The speed of the plane in the air is 200mph. This is the hypotenuse of the right triangle in the diagram above. The speed of the air is 50mph. This is the smaller leg of the same right triangle. By the Pythagorean theorem, the other leg has a length equal to $\sqrt{(200\text{mph})^2 - (50\text{mph})^2} \approx 194\text{mph}$. This means that the components of the velocity of the plane relative to the air are $\mathbf{v}'_{PLANE} = (194\text{mph E}, 50\text{mph N})$.

In terms of direction angles, the plane should choose a heading of about $14\frac{1}{2}°$ north of east (relative to the ground).

If the plane could only fly at 180mph instead of 200mph, how would the desired heading change? (In other words, would the direction be closer to east, farther from east, or the same direction as before?)

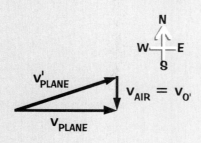

Answer. The speed and the direction of the moving air stay the same, and the direction of $\mathbf{v}_{PLANE}$ also stays the same. The primary change is to the magnitude of $\mathbf{v}'_{PLANE}$. As this vector gets smaller, while keeping the resultant velocity pointing east, $\mathbf{v}'_{PLANE}$ points more northward, so if the plane could only fly at 180mph, the heading would be farther from east.

Note that the *heading* is literally the direction in which the airplane is pointed as seen from the ground. So, even though the plane is moving directly east (relative to the ground), the airplane is pointed slightly north as shown in the diagram. The harder the wind is blowing south, the more the plane must be pointed north in order to maintain this easterly velocity (relative to the ground).

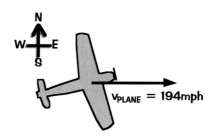

Other problems might be computationally more difficult than this one, but strategically, they are the same. If you can draw the situation, keep track of the reference frames, and keep track of which frame each particular position or velocity is measured, then most of the time, you will be able to reason toward an answer.

ROTATIONAL MOTION

Rotational motion refers to those situations in which objects are spinning. Like previous topics, new ideas are helpful for focusing attention on relevant features, for describing the motion of spinning objects, and for explaining the behavior of spinning objects.

Unlike previous topics, rotational motion involves a wide range of new ideas and new principles. A complete study would require a development roughly equivalent to the development of linear motion in the first three volumes of **Minds•On Physics**. Instead we will devote only 8 activities and about 20 pages of this Reader to rotational motion. This means we will not cover everything, and it will not be covered in as much depth as we have covered other topics. However, we would like you to understand as much as possible in the small space we have. There are two ways we are going to accomplish this.

First, we are going to make frequent analogies to linear motion, and rely heavily on your understanding and appreciation of linear motion ideas and principles. In other words, nearly everything you have learned about position, velocity, acceleration, forces, and energy will be used to "speed up" how quickly you can learn about rotational motion.

Second, we are going to restrict the formal development to a special class of rotational motion, namely rotation about a fixed axis. This will help us to avoid some sophisticated mathematics that you probably do not know yet. As a result, some of the ideas presented and used here will not apply generally, so you must be careful when thinking about more general situations.

Although there are many new ideas and principles in rotational motion, there are no new laws. Newton's laws and conservation of momentum and energy are still needed to understand and predict the motion of objects. However, the form that these laws will take is different for rotational motion. New definitions are needed to simplify the description and explanations of motion.

There are three major subtopics within rotational motion: *angular kinematics*, *angular dynamics*, and *energy in rotating systems*. (We do not say "angular energy"; later you will find out why.) We start with angular kinematics.

2.1   ANGULAR KINEMATICS

Angular kinematics is the study of the descriptions of motion for spinning objects. It does not include any explanations of <u>why</u> spinning objects behave a certain way; that will be covered later in *angular dynamics*. For now, we are concerned only with representing the motion and changes in motion of rigid objects.

The main reason for introducing angular quantities is that when an object is rigid and turns by a certain amount, each part of the object travels different distances. This makes it difficult to apply *linear* kinematics and *linear* dynamics. (In other words, it is difficult to apply the ideas you have already learned.) Therefore, we need a new set of kinematic quantities. The quickest way to learn angular kinematics is by analogy to linear kinematics.

2.1.1   Angular vs. linear kinematics. For linear motion, we have three motion quantities, position x, velocity v_x, and acceleration a_x. The velocity is the rate at which the position is changing, and the acceleration is the rate at which the velocity is changing. When the acceleration is constant, we can write relationships for the position and velocity as functions of time. All three quantities are vectors, so positive and negative are important attributes.

By convention, positive x is to the right of the origin. So, in the diagram to the right, position is positive, because the ball is to the right of the origin, but velocity is negative, because the ball is moving to the left. We know nothing about its acceleration.

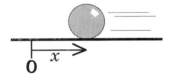

For angular motion, we also have three motion quantities: *angular position* θ ("theta"), *angular velocity* ω ("omega"), and *angular acceleration* α ("alpha"). The angular velocity is the rate at which the angular position is changing, and the angular acceleration is the rate at which the angular velocity is changing. When the angular acceleration is constant, we can write relationships for the angular position and angular velocity as functions of time. All three quantities are vectors, so positive and negative are important attributes.

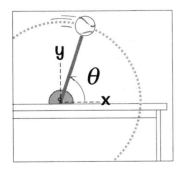

When the axis of rotation is fixed, we usually choose the origin to be at the point about which the object is rotating. By convention, we measure the angular position counterclockwise (CCW) from the positive x-axis. This means that counterclockwise rotations have a positive angular velocity and clockwise (CW) rotations have a negative angular velocity. So, in the diagram to the left, angular position is positive, but angular velocity is negative. We know nothing about the angular acceleration.

These analogies and some others are summarized in the table on the next page.

	Linear Motion	Rotational Motion (fixed axis)
MOTION QUANTITIES (SYMBOL)	position (x) velocity (v_x) acceleration (a_x)	angular position (θ) angular velocity (ω) angular acceleration (α)
DEFINITIONS	x is measured from the origin relative to the positive direction $v_x \equiv \Delta x/\Delta t$ (Δt very small) $a_x \equiv \Delta v_x/\Delta t$ (Δt very small)	θ is measured counterclockwise from the positive x-axis $\omega \equiv \Delta\theta/\Delta t$ (Δt very small) $\alpha \equiv \Delta\omega/\Delta t$ (Δt very small)
RELATIONSHIPS FOR CONSTANT ACCELERATION	$x(t) = x_0 + v_{0x}t + \tfrac{1}{2}a_x t^2$ $v_x(t) = v_{0x} + a_x t$ $(v_x)^2 = (v_{0x})^2 + 2a_x(x - x_0)$	$\theta(t) = \theta_0 + \omega_0 t + \tfrac{1}{2}\alpha t^2$ $\omega(t) = \omega_0 + \alpha t$ $(\omega)^2 = (\omega_0)^2 + 2\alpha(\theta - \theta_0)$
GRAPHS	slope of x vs. t is v_x vs. t slope of v_x vs. t is a_x vs. t area below v_x vs. t is Δx area below a_x vs. t is Δv_x	slope of θ vs. t is ω vs. t slope of ω vs. t is α vs. t area below ω vs. t is $\Delta\theta$ area below α vs. t is $\Delta\omega$

2.1.2 The radian. The proper SI unit of angular position is the *radian* (rad), where there are 2π radians in one complete revolution (360°). This means that angular velocities are measured in *radians per second* (rad/s) and angular accelerations are measured in rad/s².

The radian is different from other units of measure. Other units are based either on an arbitrary standard of measure (think of how the meter, the kilogram, and the second are defined) or are derived from these arbitrary standards (e.g., the Newton and the Joule). The degree (°) is $1/360$th of a circle, but the radian is the preferred measure of an angle, because when the radian is used, certain relationships are greatly simplified, as demonstrated below.

The ratio of the circumference C of a circle to its radius R is a constant, 2π, which is the same for all circles. ($C = 2\pi R$.) The length of an arc s is a certain fraction of the circumference, and the angle ϕ ("phi") is the same fraction of 360°:

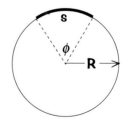

$$\frac{s}{C} = \frac{\tilde{\phi}}{360} \qquad -\text{ or }- \qquad \frac{s}{2\pi R} = \frac{\tilde{\phi}}{360}$$

where $\tilde{\phi}$ ("phi-tilde") is the <u>number</u> of degrees in the angle ϕ. (When $\phi = 30°$, $\tilde{\phi} = 30$.)

Both of these relationships are rather cumbersome. The first is cumbersome because it is often easier to determine the radius or the diameter of a circle than it is to determine its circumference. The second is cumbersome because of the factor of 2π.

However, if we use radians as a "natural" measure of the angle ϕ, the relationships become:

$$\frac{s}{C} = \frac{\tilde{\tilde{\phi}}}{2\pi} \qquad -\text{ or }- \qquad \frac{s}{R} = \tilde{\tilde{\phi}}$$

where $\tilde{\tilde{\phi}}$ ("phi-double-tilde") is the <u>number</u> of radians in the angle ϕ. (When $\phi = 2\text{rad}$, $\tilde{\tilde{\phi}} = 2$.)

In other words, the ratio of the arc length s to the radius R is equal to the number of radians in the angle ϕ. Of all the relationships between angle ϕ and arc length s, this is the simplest, and so we choose the radian as the preferred unit for describing an angle. For convenience, we usually write this relationship using the angle ϕ (rather than the dimensionless quantity $\tilde{\tilde{\phi}}$) as either $s/R = \phi$ or $s = R\phi$.

Some examples will help you to sort out the ideas covered here.

A race car is traveling at 85mph (38m/s) around a circular track with a radius of 28m. Estimate the angle swept out by the car after one second.

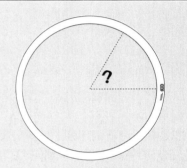

    Answer. After one second, the car has moved a distance of 38m. This is the arc length s. The radius is given as 28m, so the angle ϕ is equal to $s/R = (38\text{m}) / (28\text{m}) = 1.36$ radians. (This is about 78°.)

How long does it take the car to sweep out an angle of 160°?

    Answer. The distance traveled for an angle of 160° is $s = R\phi \approx (28\text{m})(2.8\text{rad}) \approx 78\text{m}$. At 38m/s, it takes about $(78\text{m}) / (38\text{m/s}) \approx 2$ seconds to sweep out an angle of 160°.

There are two important features to notice here. First, $s/R = \phi$ and $s = R\phi$ are not proper relationships, in the sense that, for each one, the units on the left-hand side are not equal to the units on the right-hand side. To make them proper, we must insert or drop the units of radians whenever the answer would not make sense otherwise. For instance, in the first example, the ratio s/R is unitless, yet the result is an angle, so radians are added to the answer. In the second example, the product $R\phi$ has units of m·rad, yet the result is a distance, so radians are dropped from the answer. Second, these relationships between angle, radius, and arc length only make sense when radians are used to measure the angle. We cannot use degrees or any other measure of angle.

2.1.3 Reasoning with angular kinematics ideas. We can learn a lot about rotating systems by reasoning about them. Being able to interpret angular motion quantities is often the first step in analyzing the motion of rotating objects or systems.

Estimate the angular velocity (due to a spinning Earth) of someone standing in South America at the equator (as shown at the X).

Answer. The angular velocity is the rate at which the angular position is changing. But what is the angular position in this case? The more familiar view of the Earth is from the side, as shown, and as the Earth spins, the person moves to the right along the dotted line. But view the Earth from one of the poles and now the person is moving in a circle. The rotation of the

Earth is from west to east, so as viewed from above the North Pole, rotations are counterclockwise. This means that the angular velocity is positive.

The Earth completes one revolution (2π radians) in one day (24 hours = 86,400 seconds), so the rate at which the angular position is changing is 2π rad / 86,400s = 0.000073rad/s $\approx 10^{-4}$rad/s.

Note that the angular velocity is the same for everyone on the Earth, and that it is very small. Also, the angular velocity is constant, so the angular acceleration is zero.

Angular velocity and linear velocity are very different quantities. Consider the same situation.

Estimate the speed of someone standing in South America.

Answer. Although the person is not moving relative to the surface of the Earth, he is moving very quickly relative to the center of the Earth. (See the "top view" in the previous example.)

The person completes one revolution every day (24 hours = 86,400 seconds). The total distance traveled is the circumference of the Earth at the equator (about 40,000km = 4×10^7m), so the average speed is about 460m/s (over 1000mph). Because the speed of the person is constant, the average speed is equal to the instantaneous speed. (Note that we are ignoring the speed of the Earth relative to the Sun.)

Even though the rate at which the Earth is spinning is very small ($<10^{-4}$rad/s), the linear speed of someone on the equator is large because the circumference of the circle traced out by the person is so large. Also, because the linear velocity is changing direction, the linear acceleration is non-zero, even though the linear speed is constant.

Every point on a <u>rigid</u>, spinning object has the same angular velocity, but linear velocity depends on where the point is located on the object. For instance, every point on the surface of the Earth is about the same distance from its center, but different distances from the axis of rotation. The linear velocity depends on the *latitude*.

Estimate the speed of someone sitting at the northern tip of Scotland.

Answer. Like the first example in this section, a "top" view is best. The tip of Scotland is at a latitude of about 60°N, which means that it is much closer to the axis of rotation than a point on the equator. The radius of this circle is about half as large as the radius at the equator, so its circumference is about 20,000km (instead of 40,000km). It still takes 1 day to complete the circle, so the speed of the person is about 230m/s (more than 500mph).

Some points have zero velocity. For instance, someone standing at the North Pole is not moving relative to the center of the Earth, but he is spinning at the same rate as the Earth.

2.1.4 Solving problems in angular kinematics. Common sense notions of speed, average speed, distance, and time can yield some useful results, as shown in this example.

What is the relationship between linear speed and angular speed for a spinning object? What are the relevant features?

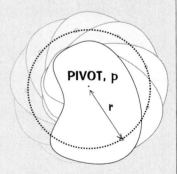

Answer. Consider an object spinning with angular speed ω about the pivot p, as shown. Choose an arbitrary point a distance r away from the pivot. The object completes 2π radians during each revolution. In other words, $\omega = 2\pi/T$, where T is the time it takes to complete 1 revolution.

The point of interest travels a distance of $2\pi r$ during the same time interval. This means that the speed of the point is $v = 2\pi r/T$, which is equal to $r\omega$.

The relevant feature is the distance r between the pivot and the point of interest.

The relationship $v = r\omega$ can be verified using either of the last two examples in the previous section. Note that $\omega = 2\pi/T$ and $v = r\omega$ are like other relationships involving both angular and linear quantities: They are not proper relationships, because the units are different on the two sides of each equation. Radians must be added or dropped to make sure the final result makes sense.

Like linear motion problems, graphs can help organize information, focus your attention on relevant features, and make it easier to solve for the desired unknown.

A popular amusement park ride is made from a large barrel that spins about its center using a motor. People stand against the inside wall of the barrel, which accelerates at about $1/10$ rad/s² until it is spinning once every 2 seconds. 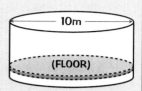 When the barrel is spinning at its fastest, the floor drops out from underneath the people, but they do not fall. Instead, they seem to be "stuck" to the wall. After a short time, the floor is brought back, and the barrel slows down at twice the rate as before. If the entire ride lasts about 3 minutes, how long is the barrel spinning at maximum speed, and how many revolutions do the people make during the entire ride?

Answer. This is a kinematics problem because only the information about angular acceleration and angular velocity is relevant. In other words, we do not need to analyze the forces involved here, and we do not care what the dimensions are for the barrel. A graph of angular velocity vs. time will help us solve this problem.

The slope at the beginning of the graph is equal to the given angular acceleration 0.1rad/s², and the graph reaches a maximum at ω_{max} = 1rev / 2s = 2πrad / 2s ≈ 3.1rad/s. The change in ω is +3.1rad/s, so at 0.1rad/s², it takes about 31 seconds to reach maximum speed.

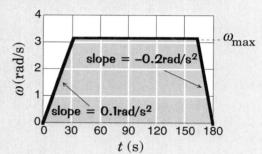

The slope at the end is negative and twice as large as the initial slope. The change in ω is −3.1rad/s, so at −0.2rad/s², it takes only about 16 seconds to stop. The total time is 180s, so they spend 47s speeding up or slowing down, and almost 2¼ minutes at maximum speed.

To find the number of revolutions that the people rotate through, we need the angular displacement. This is the area below ω vs. t for the relevant time period, which is shown in gray. The total is about 491 radians, or just over 78 revolutions.

Note that even though the people are slowing down during the last 31 seconds, they still have a positive angular displacement. Also, graphs of angular velocity vs. time are particularly useful for solving angular kinematics problems, because the slope of ω vs. t is angular acceleration α, and the area below ω vs. t is the angular displacement $\Delta\theta$.

Before solving angular motion problems, it is often useful to consider an analogous linear motion problem, and think about how you would solve it. Keep in mind that the relationships derived for both linear and angular motion require the acceleration to be constant.

2.2 ANGULAR DYNAMICS

Angular dynamics is the study of <u>why</u> rotating systems behave a certain way. We <u>could</u> use forces and linear accelerations, but this is difficult, primarily because it is often inconvenient to isolate individual parts of a spinning object. Treating the entire object as a whole is much more practical for explaining its behavior.

2.2.1 Pivots. As mentioned earlier, we are assuming that motion is restricted to rotations about a fixed axis, in order to avoid sophisticated mathematics that you probably do not know yet. The idea of a *pivot* will help explain and simplify this approach. Consider an example.

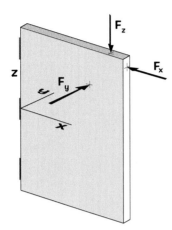

A door is hinged as shown, and three forces are exerted at various locations on the door. For convenience, we choose the z-axis to be along the (fixed) axis of rotation, and the x- and y-axes to be parallel to the floor. Thus, F_x and F_y are parallel to the floor, and F_z is parallel to the axis of rotation.

Experience tells us that F_z has no effect on the motion of the door. In other words, without the hinges, F_z would cause rotations about the y-axis, but the hinges prevent the door from spinning that way. Therefore, only F_x and F_y can affect the motion of the door. A top view gives a slightly clearer picture of what is going on here.

In this view, the axis of rotation is perpendicular to the page, and F_z is dropped because it does not affect the motion of the door. (It affects only the forces exerted by the hinge.) Also in this view, we lose all information about the heights at which forces are exerted. This is okay because the heights do not affect the door's motion either.

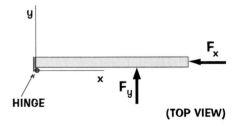

Because the axis of rotation is difficult to draw in diagrams like this one, we often refer instead to the *pivot*, which we define to be the point in the plane of the diagram about which the object rotates and through which the axis passes. Like the hinges in the example above, the pivot provides all the forces needed to make sure the object rotates <u>only</u> about the fixed axis.

For the remainder of this chapter, we will ignore any components of forces parallel to the axis of rotation (such as F_z above) and consider only those components perpendicular to the axis. Also, we will draw views of the situations in which the relevant forces are parallel to the surface of this page, and the axis of rotation is perpendicular to the page. Whenever we say "about the pivot" or "about the point p", this is simply a short-hand way of saying "about the fixed axis of rotation" or "about a fixed axis of rotation that passes through point p".

2.2.2 Torque. The rotational analog to force is called *torque*. When the torques on an object are balanced, its angular acceleration is zero, and when the torques are unbalanced, its angular acceleration is non-zero. For instance, consider the following situation. Andy and Bill are pushing on either side of a door, keeping it at rest. ω is constant, so α is zero, and the torques are balanced. If one of the boys moves farther or closer to the hinge, the door will have an angular acceleration. This means that torque depends on where the force is applied relative to the fixed axis of rotation. Also, if one of them changes how hard he is pushing, the door will have an angular acceleration. This means that torque depends on the strength of the force. Finally, if either Andy or Bill pushes at an angle (rather than perpendicular to the door as above) he would have to exert a larger force to keep the door at rest. This means that torque depends on the direction of the force.

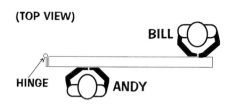

(TOP VIEW)

BILL

HINGE   ANDY

Thus, the torque depends on four factors: (1) <u>where</u> the force is applied; (2) the location of the <u>fixed axis</u>; (3) the <u>strength</u> of the force applied; and (4) the <u>direction</u> of the force applied. For rotations about a fixed axis, the definition of torque is the force multiplied the *moment arm* ($r_{\min}$), which is the <u>shortest</u> distance between the *line of force* and the pivot p:

$$\tau_p \equiv Fr_{\min}$$
        definition of torque about a fixed axis of rotation

where the Greek symbol τ ("tau") is used to represent torque, and the subscript p refers to the pivot, about which the object spins.

We can also write the definition of torque as follows:

$$\tau_p \equiv F_\perp r$$
        definition of torque about a fixed axis of rotation

where $F_\perp$ is the component of the applied force perpendicular to the line segment connecting the pivot p and the point of application, and r is the length of this line segment. (See diagram above.) These two definitions of torque yield the same result. You must decide which one is more useful for a particular circumstance.

Torque is a vector quantity. As with angular position, velocity, and acceleration, torque is positive when the force would cause a counterclockwise turn and negative when the force would cause a clockwise turn (e.g., Bill exerts a CW torque and Andy exerts a CCW torque).

The proper SI unit of torque is the Newton·meter (N·m). Even though the SI unit of energy is also N·m (i.e., 1J = 1N·m), we never use Joules to describe torques. The N·m reminds us that torque is a force multiplied by a distance. A couple of examples will help you understand how to apply the definition of torque.

A construction worker is holding a heavy steel beam as shown. If the tension in the rope is about 260N, what is the torque exerted by the worker as measured relative to the base of the beam?

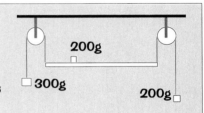

Answer. You might think that complicated geometry and trigonometry are needed to answer this question. Geometry and trigonometry <u>could</u> be used, but they are not necessary because the given diagram is a scale drawing.

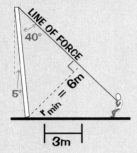

To determine the torque, we need to identify the line of force and the moment arm (r_{min}). A measurement of the length of the moment arm yields a value of about 6m, so the torque about the base of the beam is $Fr_{min} = (260N) \times (6m) = 1,560N \cdot m$. The direction of this torque is clockwise.

The direction of the torque is clockwise because, in the absence of any other torques, the beam would rotate clockwise due to this torque.

An arrangement of blocks, strings and pulleys is made as shown. The 200g block is moved along the 60cm plank until the system balances, which occurs when it is 15cm from the end. Determine the torques exerted on the plank relative to its center.

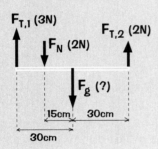

Answer. There are four forces on the plank: Two tension forces, a normal force, and a gravitational force. F_g exerts no torque about the center because the moment arm is zero. F_N and $F_{T,2}$ exert counterclockwise torques having magnitudes $2N \times 0.15m = 0.3N \cdot m$ and $2N \times 0.30m = 0.6N \cdot m$, respectively. $F_{T,1}$ exerts a clockwise torque with a magnitude of $3N \times 0.30m = 0.9N \cdot m$.

Note first that for a uniform object such as the plank, the gravitational force acts *as though* it is exerted at the center of the object. We are not given the mass of the plank, but we can still determine the torque due to gravitation because the moment arm is zero. However, we can use Newton's 2nd law to determine the mass of the plank. Because the plank is not accelerating, the net force on the plank is zero, which means that the four forces must balance. The other three forces have a vector sum of 3N [up], so the weight of the plank must be 3N [down]. Therefore, the plank has a mass of 300g.

The *net* torque is the vector sum of all the individual torques exerted on an object.

$$\tau_{net,p} \equiv \tau_{1,p} + \tau_{2,p} + \tau_{3,p} + ...$$ **definition of net torque about a fixed axis**

Note that we have included the subscript "p" on each term to remind us that the torque depends on the location of the pivot.

2.2.3 Moment of inertia.

The rotational analog to mass is called *moment of inertia*. It is a measure of how difficult it is to get an object spinning about a particular axis. For instance, consider the two arrangements of coins shown to the right. There are the same number of coins in each, so they have the same mass. But disk A is easier to get spinning, because its moment of inertia is smaller.

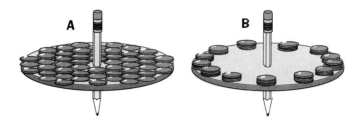

(In other words, the same torque applied to both disks produces a larger angular acceleration for disk A, even though they both have the same total mass.) The moment of inertia depends on how the mass is distributed. In particular, the farther the mass is located from the axis of rotation, the larger the moment of inertia is.

The moment of inertia depends on the axis about which it is measured. For instance, a stick

p _____ c _____ q

$I_c < I_p = I_q$

is easier to get spinning about its center than about either of its ends ($I_c < I_p = I_q$). The moment of inertia also depends on the mass. The larger the mass (of the stick, for example), the larger its moment of inertia. In other words, for a fixed torque, the larger the mass, the smaller the resulting angular acceleration.

Thus, the moment of inertia depends on three factors: (1) the <u>distribution</u> of mass; (2) the <u>axis</u> about which moment of inertia is measured; and (3) the <u>amount</u> of mass. The definition of moment of inertia is the mass of an object multiplied by the square of the distance the mass is from the axis of rotation.

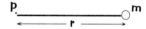

$$I_p \equiv mr^2$$ **definition of moment of inertia (point mass)**

As before, the subscript p reminds us that the moment of inertia depends on the location of the pivot. This definition applies only when <u>all</u> of the mass is the same distance r from the pivot.

When the mass is distributed, as is the case for disk A above, you must treat different parts of the disk separately and add up the contributions from each.

$$I_p \equiv m_a r_a^2 + m_b r_b^2 + m_c r_c^2 + ...$$ **definition of moment of inertia (composite object)**

where $a, b, c, ...$ refer to different masses or different parts of a rigid object.

Some examples will help you to apply the definition of moment of inertia.

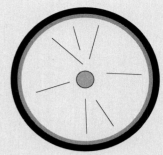

Estimate the moment of inertia of a bicycle wheel about its center.

Answer. Almost all of the mass of a bicycle wheel is located at the rim, so all we need to know is the mass and the radius of the wheel. A standard wheel has a diameter of 27 inches (just over 68cm) and a mass of about 5kg.

Even though this is a composite object, the moment of inertia is the same as if all the mass were located at a point on the rim, a distance of 34cm from the center. So, $I_{center} = MR^2 = (5kg) \times (0.34m)^2 \approx 0.6kg \cdot m^2$.

Three point masses are located in front of a grid as shown. Each pair is connected by a light rod. Masses *a* and *c* are 2kg each, and mass *b* is 4kg. Determine the moments of inertia for rotations about each of the masses.

Answer. First, we must assume that rotations occur in the plane of the grid, through axes perpendicular to the page. Second, we note that the rods do not contribute because they are "light" which means "massless". Third, we note that the distance between each mass and itself is zero, so if we ignore the size of each mass, it does not contribute significantly to the moment of inertia about itself. Only the other two masses contribute.

So, we will determine the squared distances (r^2) for each pair of masses using the Pythagorean theorem, then apply the definition of the moment of inertia for a composite object. About mass *a*, the distance to mass *b* is $\sqrt{5}$m, and the distance to mass *c* is 3m, so the moment of inertia is $I_a = (4kg) \times (5m^2) + (2kg) \times (9m^2) = 38kg \cdot m^2$. About mass *b*, the answer is $I_b = (2kg) \times (5m^2) + (2kg) \times (8m^2) = 26kg \cdot m^2$. About mass *c*, the answer is $I_c = (2kg) \times (9m^2) + (4kg) \times (8m^2) = 50kg \cdot m^2$.

Find the moment of inertia about the axis passing through masses *a* and *c*.

Answer. Only mass *b* contributes to this moment of inertia. It is 2m from the axis of rotation, so the moment of inertia is $I_{ac} = (4kg) \times (4m^2) = 16kg \cdot m^2$.

Note that we have ignored the distribution of each mass about its own center. Because the masses have relatively small radii (compared to the distances between masses), the contributions to the total moments of inertia are small. Also, in the last example, the axis of rotation is not perpendicular to the page.

2.2.4 Newton's 2nd law in rotational form. A net force on an object causes it to accelerate. Likewise, a net torque on an object causes an angular acceleration. The proportionality constant for Newton's 2nd law in linear form is the mass m. The proportionality constant for Newton's 2nd law in rotational form is the moment of inertia I. Mathematically,

$$\tau_{net,p} = I_p \alpha_p \qquad\qquad \text{\textbf{Newton's 2nd law in rotational form}}$$

Note that the subscript p is used to indicate that the axis of rotation is fixed, and to remind us that the net torque and the moment of inertia depend on the location and orientation of the axis of rotation.

2.2.5 Angular vs. linear dynamics. Just as in angular kinematics, there are many analogies between linear dynamics and angular dynamics. These analogies are summarized in the table below. Keep in mind that the goal of kinematics is to describe the motion of objects, but the goal here is to explain <u>why</u> rotating systems behave the way they do and to predict the motion of objects.

	Linear Dynamics	Angular Dynamics	(comments)
QUANTITIES (SYMBOL)	force ($\mathbf{F}$)	torque (τ)	
	mass (m)	moment of inertia (I)	
DEFINITIONS		$\tau_p \equiv F r_{min} = F_\perp r$	(direction by common sense)
	$\mathbf{F}_{net} \equiv \mathbf{F}_1 + \mathbf{F}_2 + ...$	$\tau_{net,p} \equiv \tau_{1,p} + \tau_{2,p} + ...$	
		$I_p \equiv m r^2$	(point object)
	$M \equiv m_a + m_b + ...$	$I_p \equiv m_a r_a^2 + m_b r_b^2 + ...$	(composite objects)
NEWTON'S 2ND LAW	$\mathbf{F}_{net} = m\,\mathbf{a}$	$\tau_{net,p} = I_p \alpha_p$	(fixed axis of rotation)

Note that torque, net torque, and moment of inertia depend on the location of the fixed axis (through the pivot p). Also, this way of writing Newton's 2nd law in rotational form applies only when the axis of rotation is fixed.

2.2.6 Reasoning with angular dynamics ideas. Some reasoning exercises will help develop some intuition about torque, net torque, and moment of inertia, as well as their relationships to angular acceleration.

When an object is at rest, its angular velocity is constant and its angular acceleration is zero, so the net torque about <u>any</u> axis must be zero also. In other words, every axis is a fixed axis, so torques may be calculated relative to any axis. Consider the following example.

A 1kg mass is suspended from a light rod as shown. Which string has the smallest tension?

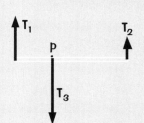

string #1   string #2
string #3

Answer. There are three strings to consider. Let's focus on the rod. Only three forces are exerted on the rod, one due to each string attached to it. (The rod is "light" so it is considered massless.) All three forces are vertical, and they must balance, so the tension in string #3 is the largest. This means one of the other two must have the smallest tension.

Taking torques about point p, only strings 1 and 2 exert non-zero torques. These torques must balance, so they are equal and opposite to each other. String #2 has the larger moment arm, so it has the smaller tension in it.

Because the rod is at rest, any point may be chosen to be the pivot. The final result is the same for any choice, but some choices are better than others, as above. Also, a free-body diagram is extremely useful for answering this question. When drawing free-body diagrams, the location and direction of each force is now important, especially for determining torque.

Keep in mind that Newton's 2nd law in linear form ($\mathbf{F}_{net} = m\,\mathbf{a}$) remains an important and useful principle for analyzing systems, especially *static* systems (systems that are at rest). When an object is at rest, the torques must balance, and the forces must balance as well. Many situations require you to use both forms of Newton's 2nd law in order to understand them completely.

For a composite object, a force of gravity is exerted on each part in proportion to its mass. However, when analyzing rotational motion problems, the force of gravity acts on the whole object *as though* it is exerted through its *center of gravity* (or *balance point*). For a uniform object, this is the center of the object.

A pencil and eraser are joined as shown and balanced. Which is heavier, the pencil or the eraser?

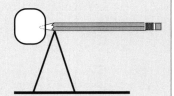

Answer. You might think that because they balance, they must have about the same weight. However, this is not right. Balance means that the <u>torques</u> are equal, not the weights. Because the center of the pencil is farther from the balance point than the center of the eraser, it must have a smaller weight, so the eraser is heavier.

Because the center of the pencil is about twice as far away from the balance point as the center of the eraser, the eraser weighs about twice as much as the pencil.

Torque and angular acceleration are vector quantities, so direction matters.

Two masses are attached to strings wound around a double pulley as shown. If the arrangement is released from rest, which direction will the pulley start to rotate?

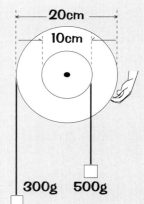

Answer. First of all, we do not need to know the mass or the moment of inertia of the pulley to answer this question. Second, we do not need to determine the torque exerted by the hand holding the pulley at rest, because the forces exerted by the hand will be removed when the pulley is released.

The hand exerts two forces on the pulley: a normal force (N_2) and a static friction force (F_{fs}). There are four more forces on the pulley: Two tension forces exerted by the strings, a gravitational force, and a normal force on the axle to keep it from falling (N_1). The torques due to gravitation and to both normal forces are zero, because the moment arms are zero for all three of these forces.

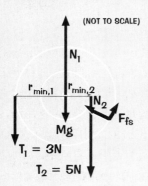

The torque exerted on the pulley by the left string is $(0.1\text{m}) \times (3\text{N}) = 0.3\text{N·m}$ CCW, and the torque exerted on the pulley by the right string is $(0.05\text{m}) \times (5\text{N}) = 0.25\text{N·m}$ CW. The torque exerted by the left string is larger than the torque exerted by the right string, so the pulley will start to rotate counterclockwise when it is released.

Even though the tension in the right string is larger, the torque it exerts is smaller, because the moment arm is sufficiently small.

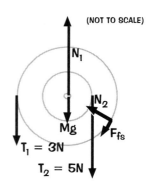

The net torque on the pulley is zero, because its angular acceleration is zero. So, the torque exerted by the hand must balance the two torques exerted by the strings. This means the hand exerts a <u>clockwise</u> torque of 0.05N·m. The normal force exerted by the hand exerts no torque, so this balancing torque is exerted by the static friction force, and the direction shown above is actually wrong. The friction force always points parallel to the surface, but in this case, it should be pointing at an angle downward, as shown to the right.

After the pulley is released, the tensions in the strings change, because the hanging masses start to accelerate. The acceleration of the left mass is downward, so the tension in the left string must be slightly <u>less</u> than 3N. The acceleration of the right mass is upward, so the tension in the right string must be slightly <u>more</u> than 5N.

2.2.7 Solving problems in angular dynamics. Problems are solved in angular dynamics just like problems in linear dynamics. The net torque is the vector sum of all the torques on the object. If you know the moment of inertia and the net torque you can determine the angular acceleration and predict the motion of the object. If you know the moment of inertia and the angular acceleration instead, you can determine the net torque.

> **Two masses are attached to strings wound around a double pulley as shown. The double pulley has a total mass of 2400g (2.4kg) and a total moment of inertia about its center of 100,000g·cm² (0.01kg·m²). If the arrangement is released from rest, estimate the angular acceleration of the double pulley.**
>
>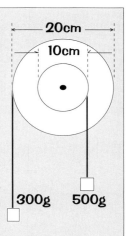
>
> *Answer.* First of all, the angular acceleration is constant, so it does not matter that the arrangement is released from rest. The answer is the same for any initial condition. Second, the tensions in the strings are <u>approximately</u> equal to the weights of the hanging masses, so we will use these weights to <u>estimate</u> the torques exerted by the two strings. At the end, we will check this assumption.
>
> There are four forces on the pulley: Two tension forces exerted by the strings, a gravitational force, and a normal force on the axle to keep it from falling. The torques about the center of the pulley due to gravitation and the normal force are zero, because the moment arms are zero for both these forces. The torque about the center exerted by the left string is $(0.1\text{m}) \times (3\text{N}) = 0.3\text{N·m}$ CCW, and the torque
>
>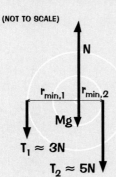
>
> about the center exerted by the right string is $(0.05\text{m}) \times (5\text{N}) = 0.25\text{N·m}$ CW, for a net torque of 0.05N·m CCW. This means that the angular acceleration of the pulley is in the counterclockwise direction. Mathematically,
>
> $$\tau_{net,c} = I_c \alpha_c$$
>
> where c refers to the center of the pulley.
> Solving for α_c, we get
>
> $$\begin{aligned} \alpha_c &= \tau_{net,c} / I_c \\ &\approx (0.05\text{N·m CCW}) / (0.01\text{kg·m}^2) \\ &\approx 5\text{rad/s}^2 \text{ CCW} \end{aligned}$$

Note first that $1\text{N} = 1\text{kg·m/s}^2$, so $(1\text{N·m}) / (1\text{kg·m}^2) = 1/\text{s}^2$. The proper unit for angular acceleration is rad/s^2, so radians are inserted into the final numerical value. The linear acceleration of the hanging masses are equal to $a = r\alpha$, where r is the radius of the pulley it is hanging from. So, $a_1 = (0.10\text{m}) \times (5\text{rad/s}^2) = 0.5\text{m/s}^2$, and $a_2 = (0.05\text{m}) \times (5\text{rad/s}^2) = 0.025\text{m/s}^2$. These are small compared to g, so the approximation above is valid. Note that the two accelerations are different, because the masses are attached to pulleys of different radii.

2.3 ENERGY IN ROTATIONAL SYSTEMS

Just as in angular kinematics and dynamics, there are analogies between energy as you have learned it so far and energy in rotating systems. One important difference here is that there are no new concepts to introduce. What is new is how the old ideas are applied.

2.3.1 Kinetic energy of rotating objects. Rotating objects have kinetic energy because mass is moving. The type of energy is the same as the energy in an object moving in a straight line. No new quantities need to be defined in order to find the kinetic energy of a rotating object. We will show how to write the kinetic energy of a spinning object in terms of the moment of inertia and the angular speed.

When a rigid object is spinning about an axis, the speed of each point depends on how far it is

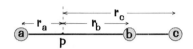

from the axis of rotation ($v = r\omega$). So, for example, when the arrangement on the left is spinning, mass a is moving the slowest because it is closest to the pivot p, and mass c is moving the fastest because it is farthest from p.

When there are many masses moving, we add up the contributions from each individual mass:

$$E_K \equiv \tfrac{1}{2}m_a v_a{}^2 + \tfrac{1}{2}m_b v_b{}^2 + \ldots \qquad \textbf{definition of kinetic energy for multiple masses}$$

where a, b, etc. refer to individual masses.

For a rigid object spinning about point p at angular speed ω_p, we can re-write E_K as:

$$E_K = \tfrac{1}{2}\big(m_a r_a{}^2 + m_b r_b{}^2 + \ldots\big)\omega_p{}^2 \qquad \textbf{kinetic energy for spinning composite object}$$

where v_a is replaced by $r_a\omega_p$, etc., and common factors of $\tfrac{1}{2}$ and $\omega_p{}^2$ are separated out.

The term in parentheses above is what we defined previously to be the moment of inertia about the fixed axis through the pivot p. This means we can simplify this expression:

$$E_K = \tfrac{1}{2}I_p\,\omega_p{}^2 \qquad \textbf{kinetic energy for object rotating about fixed axis}$$

Note that this expression does <u>not</u> take into account linear motion of the system, for instance, if the axis is moving also.

2.3.2 Potential energy in rotational systems. Rotating systems can also contain potential energy. For instance, when a string or rubber band is twisted, potential energy is stored in it, much like potential energy is stored in a spring. When the torque is proportional to the angular displacement of the string from equilibrium (that is, $\tau = K\theta$), the energy stored in the string is $\tfrac{1}{2}K\theta^2$. (This set-up is sometimes called a *torsional spring*.)

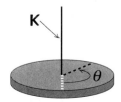

2.3.3 Energy for linear vs. rotational motion. Here is a summary of how energy ideas are applied to rotating systems.

	Linear Motion	Rotational Motion (fixed axis)
KINETIC ENERGY (rigid body)	$E_K = \frac{1}{2}mv^2$	$E_K = \frac{1}{2}I\omega^2$
ELASTIC FORCE / TORQUE	$F = kx$	$\tau = K\theta$
ELASTIC POTENTIAL ENERGY	$U_{\text{elastic}} = \frac{1}{2}kx^2$	$U_{\text{elastic}} = \frac{1}{2}K\theta^2$

Note again the similarities between linear motion and rotational motion. Keep in mind that the relationship for kinetic energy in linear motion assumes that the rigid body is not rotating, and the relationship for kinetic energy in rotational motion assumes that the axis of the rotating rigid body is not moving. We <u>never</u> refer to "angular energy" because there are no new types of energy here. For instance, potential energy in a spring can be converted to kinetic energy of a spinning object.

2.3.4 Reasoning with energy ideas in rotational systems. When you do not need to know how long a process lasts or when you do not know the exact values of forces, energy ideas are often preferred for reasoning, as shown below.

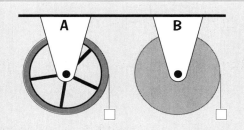

Two arrangements, A and B, are shown to the right. Both wheels have the same mass, and the hanging masses are identical. The only difference is that wheel B is solid, while wheel A is not. If both masses are released from rest at the same time, which wheel is spinning faster when its hanging mass lands on the ground?

> ***Answer.*** Energy is conserved in both systems, and no energy is transferred to the microscopic realm. Wheel A has the larger moment of inertia about its center, because its mass is located farther from the axis of rotation. The changes in gravitational potential energy are the same for both systems, so the kinetic energies of both systems are the same when the masses hit. Because wheel A has the larger moment of inertia, it must be spinning slower than wheel B. Wheel B is spinning faster when mass B hits the ground.

We <u>could</u> have used angular dynamics and kinematics to answer this question, but energy ideas are better because then we do not need to resort to equations. In other words, an explanation using only reasoning is easier with energy ideas than with dynamics and/or kinematics ideas. Try to answer this same question without using energy ideas, and you will find that the solution is long and complicated.

The idea of *center of gravity* was introduced earlier to help you determine the torque exerted by the gravitational force. In the next example, the same idea is used to determine the change in gravitational potential energy.

A hoop (A), a disk (B), and a ball on a string (C) are held as shown and released from rest. All three have the same mass. A and B have the same diameter *d*, and the string in C has length *d*. Which object has the most kinetic energy when it reaches its lowest point?

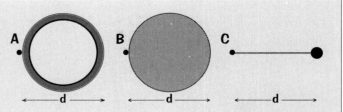

> **Answer.** You might think that all three have the same change in potential energy, but that is not quite right. In C, all of the mass is located a distance *d* from the pivot. When C reaches its lowest position, all the mass falls a distance *d*. (See diagram below.) In A and B, only a small fraction of the total mass is located a distance *d* from the pivot. The rest of the mass is closer to the pivot, so when A or B falls, the change in height of most of the mass is less than *d*.
>
>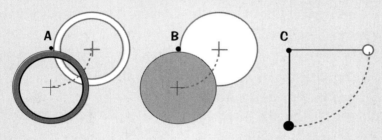
>
> The force of gravitation acts *as though* through the center of gravity of the object. These are uniform objects, so the center of gravity is at the geometric center of each one. For A and B, the change in height of the center of gravity is only half as much as the change in height for C. Energy is conserved in all three situations, so object C has the most kinetic energy when it reaches its lowest point.

Because objects A and C have the same mass and the same change in height, they have the same change in U_g. Therefore, they also have the <u>same</u> kinetic energy when they reach their lowest point, even though they have <u>different</u> moments of inertia relative to the pivot.

Also, the center of gravity for the hoop is at the center of the hoop, even though there is no mass there. This is because gravitation is not actually exerting a force at the center of gravity; it is exerting individual forces on individual parts of the hoop. The overall effect is the same as a single force exerted at the center of gravity.

2.3.5 Solving problems with energy ideas in rotational systems. When solving problems, Conservation of Energy and the Work–Kinetic Energy Theorem are applied in the same way as before. The only difference is that you must consider new and different sources of kinetic and potential energy. In other words, there is nothing called "angular" energy, and "angular" energy is not conserved. There is just kinetic and potential energy. In the example below, gravitational potential energy is converted to kinetic energy of a falling mass <u>and</u> kinetic energy of a wheel.

A wheel having mass M and radius R is hung from the ceiling as shown. A string is wound around the wheel and attached to a hanging mass m. If the mass is released from rest, how fast is the wheel spinning after the hanging mass has fallen a distance h?

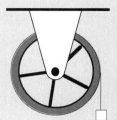

Answer. Energy is conserved, so the change in gravitational potential energy of the system is equal and opposite to the change in kinetic energy of the system. There is no change in microscopic or spring potential energy.

Taking the lowest point to be $y = 0$, the final potential energy is zero. The initial kinetic energy is zero, so:

$$\Delta E_{total} = 0$$

$$\Delta U_g + \Delta U_s + \Delta E_{micro} + \Delta E_K = 0$$

$$mg(0 - h) + (0) + (0) + (1/2 I_{wheel}\omega^2 + 1/2 mv^2 - 0) = 0$$

The only unknowns in this relationship are I_{wheel}, ω, and v. The moment of inertia I_{wheel} can be estimated from the mass and the radius of the wheel, because almost all of the mass is located a distance R from the pivot. That leaves v and ω.

The speed of the hanging mass is related to the angular speed of the wheel because the string becomes unwound as the wheel turns. (For instance, when the wheel turns 2π rad, the hanging mass falls $2\pi R$.) This means that $\Delta y = R\Delta\theta$, and also that $v = R\omega$ (because $v = \Delta y/\Delta t$, and $\omega = \Delta\theta/\Delta t$).

So, substituting $I_{wheel} \approx MR^2$ and $v = R\omega$, and then solving for ω, we get:

$$\omega = \sqrt{\frac{2mgh}{(m + M)R^2}} = \text{final angular speed of the wheel}$$

For M = 5kg, R = 35cm, m = 100g, and h = 2m, what are the final values of ω and v for this situation?

Answer. Substituting these values into the expression above, we get $\omega \approx 2.5$rad/s. For the final speed, we use $v = R\omega$ to get $v \approx 0.9$m/s.

As in many problems involving energy, we <u>could</u> have used angular dynamics and angular kinematics, but it is much easier to use energy ideas. Also, keep in mind that the units of "radians" are inserted or removed whenever appropriate. In this case, they are inserted into the final value of the angular speed, because the answer would not make sense otherwise.

In the next problem, we <u>cannot</u> use dynamics and kinematics because the net torque on the system is not constant. However, energy ideas remain useful.

A hoop of mass M and radius R is pivoted at its edge and held horizontally as shown. If the hoop is released from rest, what is its maximum angular speed? (For this situation, the moment of inertia about the pivot p is approximately $I_p = 2MR^2$.)

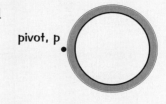
pivot, p

> **Answer.** The maximum angular speed occurs when the hoop is at its lowest position. Changes occur only in the kinetic and gravitational potential energies. The change in height of the hoop is $-R$.
>
> $$\Delta E_{total} \; = \; 0$$
>
> $$\Delta U_g + \Delta U_s + \Delta E_{micro} + \Delta E_K \; = \; 0$$
>
> $$Mg(-R) + (0) + (0) + (\tfrac{1}{2}I_p\,\omega_{max}^2 - 0) \; = \; 0$$
>
> The only unknown in this relationship is ω_{max}. So, substituting $I_p = 2MR^2$ and solving for ω_{max}, we get:
>
> $$\omega_{max} \; = \; \sqrt{g/R} \; = \; \text{maximum angular speed of the hoop.}$$

This answer does not depend on the mass of the hoop.

2.4 SOLVING PROBLEMS IN ROTATIONAL MOTION

To solve a problem in rotational motion, you must first decide what concepts are most useful: kinematics, dynamics, or energy. Remember that in each case, you must be able to apply the relevant definitions, such as torque, net torque, moment of inertia, and kinetic energy. If you are going to use angular kinematics, make sure the angular acceleration is constant; otherwise, the relationships we derived are not valid.

This completes the **Minds•On Physics** volume on *Advanced Topics in Mechanics*. We hope you have seen how wide a variety of contexts can be analyzed and understood using the basic concepts of Newtonian Mechanics: kinematics, dynamics, and conservation laws. At times, new ideas are needed to help focus your attention on new features of a situation, but the fundamental approach remains the same: Analyze first using concepts, then reason toward an answer, and only at the end, and only if necessary, apply equations to determine a final result. You should find this approach useful for any future problem or situation you encounter.

The University of Massachusetts Physics Education Research Group is dedicated to research into the cognitive processes that affect learning, communicating about, and solving problems in physics; to development of exemplary curriculum materials that maximize student motivation and learning; and to helping educators learn how to apply research results to their everyday classroom practices.

 Our logo highlights the value of structured knowledge for proficient problem solving and deep conceptual understanding. It also highlights the value of communication among students as well as communication between the teacher and individual students.